THE AMAZING COLLECTION™

D1312299

THE PENTATEUCH

SET I

THE
AMAZING
COLLECTION™

THE PENTATEUCH

GENESIS, EXODUS, LEVITICUS,

NUMBERS, AND DEUTERONOMY

SET 1

BIG
DREAM
MINISTRIES

© 2004 by Big Dream Ministries, Inc.

No part of *The Amazing Collection*, whether audio, video, or print, may be reproduced in any form without written permission from Big Dream Ministries, Inc., P.O. Box 324, 12460 Crabapple Road, Suite 202, Alpharetta, Georgia 30004
1-678-366-3460
www.theamazingcollection.org

ISBN 1-932199-01-2

Cover design by Brand Navigation and Arvid Wallen
Cover composite image by Getty Images and Corbis
Creative Team: Leigh McLeroy, Kathy Mosier, Pat Reinheimer, Glynese Northam

Some of the anecdotal illustrations in this book are true to life and are included with the permission of the persons involved. All other illustrations are composites of real situations, and any resemblance to people living or dead is coincidental.

Unless otherwise identified, all Scripture quotations in this publication are taken from the *New American Standard Bible* (NASB), © The Lockman Foundation 1960, 1962, 1963, 1968, 1971, 1972, 1973, 1975, 1977, 1995.

Printed in Canada

2 3 4 5 6 7 8 9 10 / 08 07 06 05

Welcome to
The Amazing Collection
The Bible, Book by Book

It is amazing how a love letter arriving at just the right time can gladden the heart, refresh the soul, and restore the passion of the beloved. When lovers are separated by distance and can communicate only through the written word, that word becomes the lifeline of their love.

The greatest love letter ever written often sits on our shelves unopened as we go about our lives, sometimes fearful, burdened, anxious, in pain, and in doubt, not knowing that on its pages we can find all we need to live the life we have always wanted.

In this love letter we will discover God, and through Him we will receive hope, assurance, freedom from fear, guidance for everyday life, wisdom, joy, peace, power, and above all, the way to salvation. We will find the life we have always longed for — *abundant* life.

The Bible is simply a love letter compiled into sixty-six books and written over a period of sixteen hundred years by more than forty authors living on three continents. Although the authors came from different backgrounds, there is one message, one theme, one thread that runs throughout the entire Bible from the first book, Genesis, to the last book, Revelation. That message is God's redeeming love for mankind — a message that is as relevant for us today as it was two thousand years ago.

God has written the Bible so that men and women might enter into an intimate relationship with Him and see His character, His works, His power, and His love. It would be tragic to read these books and never come to know your God! Therefore, as you go through this study, listen to the lectures, read the Scripture, and do your daily homework. Make it your heart's desire to know God intimately. Read each page of the Bible as if it were a love letter written by the hand of God to you personally. Bask in His great love, stand in awe of His mighty power, bow before His majesty, and give thanksgiving and adoration to the One who is all-present, all-knowing, all-merciful, and all-loving. He is on every page, and He is speaking to you.

The Bible is a book inspired by God Himself. It is His story, His love letter, His invitation to you to become His child through His Son, Jesus Christ. It is the Word of God . . . indeed, the most Amazing Collection.

CONTENTS

MAPS, CHARTS, AND DIAGRAMS

WORKBOOK GUIDE

The Amazing Collection is a study of the Bible, book by book. This study focuses on the first five books of the Bible known as The Pentateuch. The following will acquaint you with the design of this series.

One book of the Bible will be studied each week through a teaching video and a written study. The teaching video includes music to stir the heart, graphics to enlighten the mind, and a personal testimony to bring the theme of that particular book to life.

The workbook contains:

1. An introduction to summarize each book.

2. Outlines to be used while watching each of the teaching videos. The answers to the outline blanks are given during the videos and can also be found in the key at the back of your workbook.

3. *Learning for Life* discussion questions to be used after viewing the videos. (If your group is large, we recommend forming small discussion groups.)

4. Five daily lessons of homework for each book.

5. A memory verse for each book.

6. Various maps, charts, and diagrams.

7. A review at the end of each week to refresh your memory. The answers to the review are found in the *Review It!* sections in the margins at the end of the lessons for Day One through Day Four. The fifth review question is a review of the memory verse.

Before you begin the homework, ask God to show you how to apply the truths of Scripture to your own life. At the beginning of each day's lesson in the workbook, there are two choices for the daily reading. The *Complete Read* enables you to read one entire book of the Bible each week. During busy times, the *Quick Read* allows you to read a few key chapters or verses from that book. The daily lesson will require a small amount of time each day to complete. Of course, feel free to extend that time with additional study.

One of the incredible things about the Word of God is that you can read the same Scripture at different times in your life and gain new insights with each reading. God's Word is inexhaustible, and it is living; it has the power to produce life-changing results.

Our prayer for you as you begin your journey through *The Amazing Collection* is that you will learn for life the purpose, main characters, geography, and time period of every book in the Bible. But above all, we pray that you will come to know more intimately the God of the Bible, His Son Jesus Christ, and the Holy Spirit.

The Pentateuch at a Glance

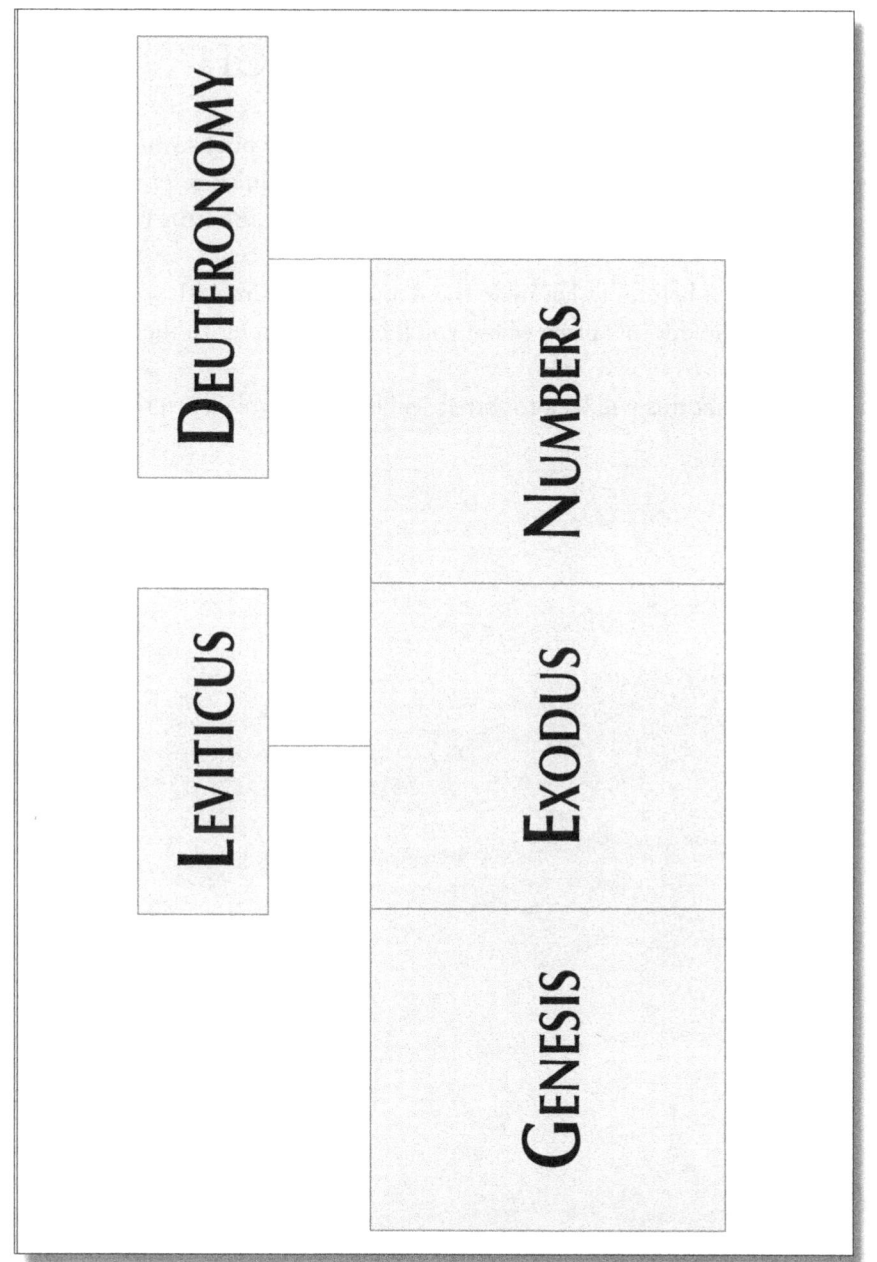

To see how these books fit into the chronology of the Old Testament books as a whole, see the chart on page 156.

Overview of THE PENTATEUCH

The following pages provide an overview of each of the books you will be studying in this set. They are designed to be cut out and used as quick reference cards with the main facts of the book on the front and the memory verse on the back.

You might find it helpful to laminate them and carry them with you on a ring or keep them in a card holder in a place where you'll be able to refer to them often.

It is our hope that this will be a tool that will help you truly learn these books for life.

GENESIS
The Book of Beginnings

WHO:	**WHAT:**	**WHERE:**
Adam	Earth Created	Garden of Eden
Noah	Man Sinned	Ur
Abraham	Earth Flooded	Canaan
Isaac	Israel Conceived	Egypt
Jacob		
Joseph		

Time Covered: 2,200 Years

EXODUS
The Book of Deliverance

WHO:	**WHAT:**	**WHERE:**
Moses	10 Plagues	Egypt
	Israel Birthed	Mount Sinai
	Red Sea	
	10 Commandments	
	Tabernacle	

Time Covered: 400 Years

LEVITICUS
The Book of Holiness

WHO:	**WHAT:**	**WHERE:**
Moses	Israel Received	Mount Sinai
Aaron	Religious Instruction	

Time Covered: 1 Month

GENESIS
The Book of Beginnings

*I will establish My covenant between Me and you
and your descendants after you.*

GENESIS 17:7

EXODUS
The Book of Deliverance

*I am the LORD your God, who brought you out of
the land of Egypt, out of the house of slavery.*

EXODUS 20:2

LEVITICUS
The Book of Holiness

You shall be holy, for I am holy.

LEVITICUS 11:45

NUMBERS
The Book of Unbelief

Who:	**What:**	**Where:**
Joshua	2 Censuses	Mount Sinai
Caleb	12 Spies	Wilderness
	Israel Rebelled Against God	Kadesh-barnea
	40 Years Wandering	Plains of Moab

Time Covered: 40 Years

DEUTERONOMY
The Book of Obedience

Who:	**What:**	**Where:**
Moses	Israel Prepared to Enter the Land	Plains of Moab
	Religious Instruction Repeated	

Time Covered: 1 Month

NUMBERS
The Book of Unbelief

Surely all the men who have seen My glory and My signs . . .
and have not listened to My voice, shall by no means see
the land which I swore to their fathers.

NUMBERS 14:22-23

DEUTERONOMY
The Book of Obedience

I have set before you life and death, the blessing and the curse.
So choose life in order that you may live.

DEUTERONOMY 30:19

Introduction to THE PENTATEUCH

This may be the first time you have come across the word *Pentateuch*, and so you may already feel like you are behind in the study. Well, take courage! This big word is derived from two Greek words that have a simple meaning. *Penta* means "five" and *teuch* means "scroll" or "book." So all together, it means "five books."

The Pentateuch was most likely written by one man, Moses. It consists of the books of Genesis, Exodus, Leviticus, Numbers, and Deuteronomy and is also known as the Law, the Torah (Hebrew for "Law"), or the Law of Moses. These books are the first five books of the seventeen Historical Books of the Old Testament and are foundational for the rest of the Bible. One book easily flows into another, developing biblical history from Creation to about 1500 BC as well as the history of Israel from the call of Abraham through the death of Moses. Here you will meet Adam, Noah, Abraham, Isaac, Jacob and his twelve sons, Moses, Aaron, and Joshua. You will travel from the Garden of Eden to Ur, Haran, Canaan, and Egypt, through the Red Sea, and on to Mount Sinai.

But the center of every book in The Pentateuch is God Almighty. Your adventure with Him will begin in the first sentence of the first book, and from there on it is a wild ride as He intervenes on behalf of men and women throughout history. You will witness His awesome power in Genesis, His desire to bring His children into liberty in Exodus, His perfect holiness in Leviticus, His justice in Numbers, and His faithfulness in Deuteronomy. You will be humbled by His mercy, awed by His compassion, frightened by His wrath, and wooed by His loving-kindness. And in every book you will come to see that Jesus Christ is concealed, ready to be revealed in the New Testament.

So hang on! It is going to be quite a study as we open the Bible, God's Amazing Collection, to the first five books: The Pentateuch.

GENESIS

[The Book of Beginnings]

I will establish My covenant between Me and you

and your descendants after you.

GENESIS 17:7

GENESIS
[The Book of Beginnings]

INTRODUCTION

Did you ever wonder how everything began? Genesis, the first book in the Bible, answers this question with startling news. It all began with the Creator, who has such power that He merely spoke and heaven and earth appeared. The plan was a good one. All creation was to live in perfect harmony—free from death, disease, violence, and fear.

Yet the first man and woman decided to disobey the very One who created them, the One who gave them the whole world except for the fruit of a single tree. With this first act of disobedience, sin entered the world and life became a constant battle as men and women suffered the consequences.

However, God in His great goodness developed a strategy to win back His children. He chose one man (Abraham) to begin a nation (Israel) that could be an example to all nations of a people living life in harmony with God. In the book of Genesis, you will meet a few of the men and women who lived during the first two millennia. You will read about their struggles and their challenges, their anguish and their joy. And above all, you will be introduced to the majesty of God, your Creator.

GENESIS
[The Book of Beginnings]

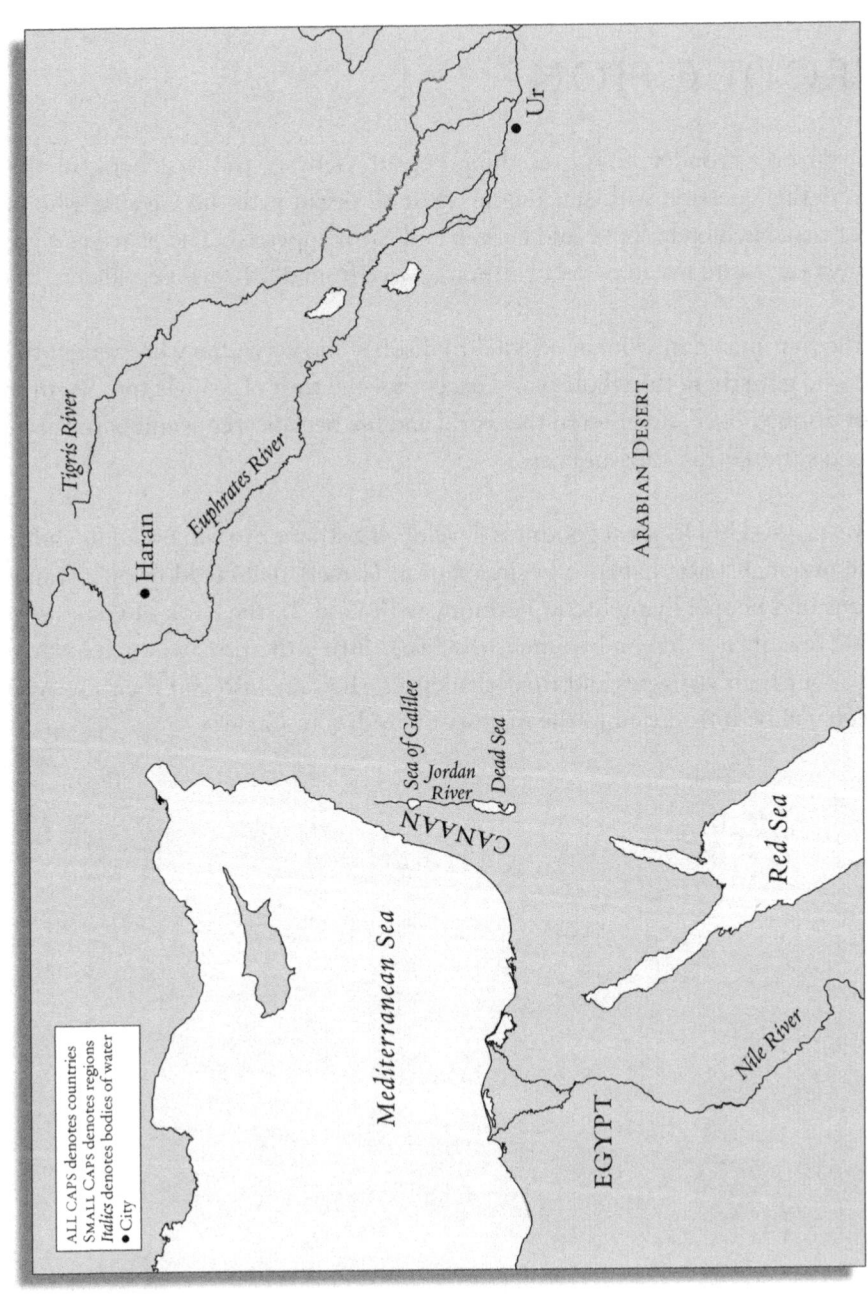

GENESIS
[The Book of Beginnings]

OVERVIEW

WHO: Author: Moses
Main Characters: Adam, Noah, Abraham, Isaac, Jacob, Joseph

WHAT: The book of beginnings

WHEN: Abraham was born approximately 2100 BC

WHERE: Garden of Eden, Ur, Canaan, Egypt

WHY: This was the beginning of man's evil heart and of the nation God established as a solution

I. **THE BEGINNING OF THE HUMAN RACE (GENESIS 1–11)**

   A. The _____ was the beginning of the universe and people (Genesis 1–2). Adam and Eve were the first man and woman. God provided a garden for them to live in perfect harmony with nature, one another, and Him.

   B. The _____ (sin) was the beginning of separation from God and physical death (Genesis 3). Eve was tempted by Satan, ate the only fruit that was off-limits, gave some to Adam, and together they rebelled against God.

   C. The _____ was the result of violence in the land that brought the judgment of God (Genesis 6–10). Noah was a righteous man who found favor with God. God instructed him to build an ark, and when the flood came, Noah and his family were saved.

   D. The beginning of languages at the Tower of Babel was the beginning of _____ (Genesis 11). God confused their language when they tried to build a monument to their own greatness.

II. **THE BEGINNING OF THE CHOSEN RACE (GENESIS 12–50)**

   God chose one man to become the father of a nation (Israel) that would love and worship God and be an example and a blessing to all the nations of the world.

   A. God made a _____ promise to Abraham (Genesis 12).

   1. Abraham's family would become a great _____.

2. All the families of the earth would be blessed by his

   _____.

3. His descendants would be given _____.

B. God's Chosen People: The Patriarchs of Israel (Genesis 21–26)

   1. The son of Abraham was _____ (Genesis 21–26).

   2. The two sons of Isaac were _____ and Esau (Genesis 27–36). Jacob was the son chosen by God to carry on the blessings of the covenant.

   3. Jacob had _____ sons who became the twelve tribes of Israel (Genesis 30–35).

   4. Jacob's favorite son was _____ (Genesis 37–50). Jacob's sons were jealous of their brother Joseph and sold him into slavery. Because God was with him, Joseph was eventually elevated to second in command in Egypt.

Joseph saved Jacob's family of seventy people from famine in Canaan by inviting them to live with him in the land of Egypt. At the end of Genesis, Jacob and Joseph had died, and the people were living in prosperity and peace in the land of Goshen in Egypt.

APPLICATION

God has created each one of His children for a unique purpose, and we are valuable in His eyes. What were you created for?

GENESIS
[The Book of Beginnings]

LEARNING FOR LIFE

1. Retell the story of Genesis (group effort).

2. What are some of the amazing facts you learned about the Bible today?

3. As you look around, how do you see that the Fall has affected mankind? Give as many examples as you can.

4. Abraham's family was a dysfunctional family in many ways. Describe some of the ways. How did God use them in spite of their problems and weaknesses?

5. In what way was Jesus involved in the creation of the world? (See John 1:1-3; Colossians 1:13-17.)

6. What were you created for? How can your gifts and talents, circumstances, and environment prepare you to serve God?

GENESIS
[The Book of Beginnings]

INTERESTING!
Genesis introduces
activities we still do
today, such as hunting
and playing musical
instruments.

DAY ONE

COMPLETE READ: Chapters 1–11
QUICK READ: Chapters 1–2

THE BIG PICTURE

Imagine opening your Bible and reading Exodus 1:1 as the very first words from God to you: "Now these are the names of the sons of Israel who came to Egypt with Jacob; they came each one with his household."

You would feel as if you had been dropped into a swirling sea of unknowns. Who is Jacob? Why does this story start in Egypt? Who are the sons of Israel and where did they come from? And that's only the book of Exodus!

Without Genesis you would wander aimlessly through the Scriptures not knowing where you had come from or where you were going. Genesis is the compass that sets us in the right direction and keeps us on course for the rest of the journey.

Based on your present knowledge of the book of Genesis, take a few moments to jot down what you wouldn't know if the Bible completely omitted Genesis and began with the book of Exodus instead.

The very same Holy Spirit who led these men to write, longs to lead us today so we can understand.

—GEORGE SWEETING, author and former president and chancellor of Moody Bible Institute

Genesis is not only the first book of the Bible and of the Old Testament; it's also the first of the Pentateuch, which is the first five foundational books (Genesis through Deuteronomy). The Pentateuch begins with Creation (Genesis 1–2) and ends with the people of Israel preparing to enter the land God has promised them (see Deuteronomy 34).

The following chart shows the Pentateuch in relation to the other sections of the Old Testament.

DID YOU KNOW?
We know very little about the history of the world in Genesis 1–11. We know much more about it in Genesis 12–50.

HISTORICAL		POETICAL	PROPHETICAL	
PENTATEUCH Genesis Exodus Leviticus Numbers Deuteronomy		Job Psalms Proverbs Ecclesiastes Song of Solomon	**MAJOR** Isaiah Jeremiah Lamentations Ezekiel Daniel	
KINGDOM Joshua Judges Ruth 1 Samuel 2 Samuel 1 Kings 2 Kings	**POST-EXILIC** 1 Chronicles 2 Chronicles Ezra Nehemiah Esther		**EARLY MINOR** Hosea Joel Amos Obadiah Jonah Micah	**LATER MINOR** Nahum Habakkuk Zephaniah Haggai Zechariah Malachi

The name *Genesis* means "beginning" and comes from the very first verse: "In the beginning God created the heavens and the earth." Moses authored Genesis, as well as the rest of the Pentateuch. Because events in the Pentateuch occurred centuries before Moses lived, he undoubtedly relied on written records and oral traditions passed down from generation to generation — and, most important, on revelation from God. The Holy Spirit superintended this monumental undertaking (see 2 Peter 1:21; 2 Timothy 3:16).

Moses most likely wrote Genesis between 1440 and 1400 BC as he led the Israelites through the wilderness on their circuitous journey from Egypt to the promised land of Canaan. Moses wrote the story of Genesis to encourage and remind the wandering, despairing Israelites that God had always been faithful to their forefathers, Abraham, Isaac, and Jacob, and would also be faithful to them.

The great majority of men are bundles of beginnings.
—RALPH WALDO EMERSON, nineteenth-century American essayist and poet

The chart that follows indicates two natural sections of the book of Genesis.

GENESIS 1–11

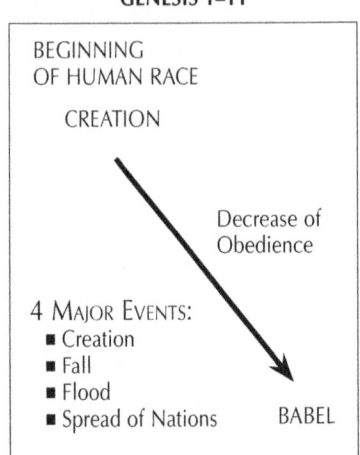

BEGINNING
OF HUMAN RACE

CREATION

Decrease of
Obedience

4 MAJOR EVENTS:
- Creation
- Fall
- Flood
- Spread of Nations   BABEL

GENESIS 12–50

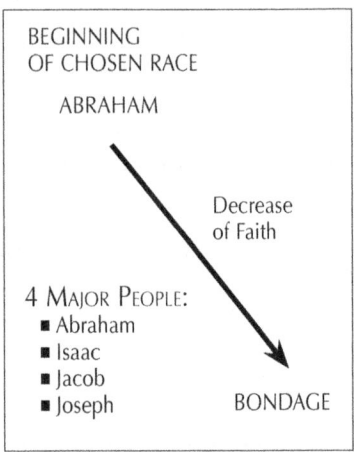

BEGINNING
OF CHOSEN RACE

ABRAHAM

Decrease
of Faith

4 MAJOR PEOPLE:
- Abraham
- Isaac
- Jacob
- Joseph   BONDAGE

As you will see over the next four days, extremely significant events take place in each of these sections. Even today we live with both the negative consequences and the positive favor of these events. The book of Genesis is not only first; it is also foundational and determinative. It establishes the beginning of blessing for all families of the earth.

In the Quick Read for today, you read the Creation account in chapters 1 and 2. Chapter 1 presents a chronological and structured description of each day of Creation. By contrast, chapter 2 presents a topical and very relaxed portrayal of the creation of man and woman.

What impressed you about God in these two chapters?

Take time to praise Him in your own way for who He reveals Himself to be in these chapters. You may want to jot down some of your thoughts, create a poem, or write a prayer. Make this very personal.

Wonder is the basis of worship.
—THOMAS CARLYLE, nineteenth-century Scottish theologian

MEMORY VERSE

I will establish My covenant between Me and you and your descendants after you.

GENESIS 17:7

REVIEW IT!
The theme of Genesis is the book of beginnings. Genesis is the beginning of blessing for all the families of the earth.

GENESIS
[The Book of Beginnings]

DAY TWO

COMPLETE READ: Chapters 12–21
QUICK READ: Chapter 3

A CRUCIAL CHAPTER

Stuart Briscoe, a pastor, author, and Englishman, writes,

> When an old lady in the Deep South asked me whether we
> have a Fourth of July in England, my immediate response
> was, "No, Madam, we go straight from the third to the
> fifth!" I learned my history in England, and when I came to
> this country, I knew so little about the events of 1776 that
> I wouldn't have recognized a Declaration of Independence
> if I'd tripped over it. But times have changed. Now I know
> that the Declaration of Independence says man has three
> inalienable rights: "life, liberty, and the pursuit of happi-
> ness." But I have often wondered why there are so many
> unhappy people in a country where freedom to pursue
> happiness is one of the most cherished rights.[1]

*God cannot give us
happiness and peace
apart from Himself,
because it is not there.
There is no such thing.*

—C. S. LEWIS, British
author and professor

Our Crucial Chapter will answer this question and also explain
why unhappiness is rampant not only in America, but across the
globe. We will see why William Shakespeare wrote, "Life is as
tedious as a twice-told tale"[2] and why Oscar Wilde wrote,
"There are only two tragedies in life: one is not getting what one
wants, and the other is getting it."[3]

Imagine Adam and Eve in Genesis 1 and 2. They were in
paradise — in perfect harmony and community with God, themselves, each other, and nature. Can you fathom a conversation like
the one that follows?

Adam: "I am so unhappy with life in this garden."
Eve: "There seems to be no way out of this humanity thing!"
Adam: "I guess we just need to grin and bear this ludicrous existence."

AMAZING! What a father-son duo! Enoch never died (Genesis 5:24), and Methuselah was the oldest man ever (Genesis 5:27).

Not a chance. Happiness defined their existence. There was no dilemma, no trace of a farce. But in Genesis 3, tragedy struck and man lost who he was created to be, becoming instead a sinner needing redemption. And God spent the next 2,000 years, one generation at a time, preparing the way for the Messiah — and for redemption — to come.

The horrible consequences of chapter 3 saturate the soul of every person born since Adam and eventually demand the death of God Himself in the person of Jesus Christ.

Read Genesis 3:1-5 and describe in your own words the serpent's temptation.

Sin isn't simply a one-dimensional deed. That's what makes it so tricky. Read Genesis 3:6 and write down the different dimensions of sin pictured there. Read 1 John 2:16 and compare the characteristics of sin portrayed there with those in Eve's experience.

The voice of sin may be loud, but the voice of forgiveness is louder.
—D. L. MOODY, nineteenth-century evangelist

What consequences of Adam and Eve's sin do you see in Genesis 3:7-13?

DID YOU KNOW?
Job was most likely a contemporary of Abraham.

God pronounced judgment on all three participants in this history-changing event. Describe the judgment on each one given in Genesis 3:14-19.

The Serpent:

Thank God for that "fine linen, clean and white, the righteousness" with which Christ covers our wounded nakedness. It becomes ours, though no thread of it was wrought in our looms.

—ALEXANDER MACLAREN, nineteenth-century British preacher

The Woman:

The Man:

But when God pronounces judgment, He also offers salvation. God is a God of redemption, of reclaiming, of saving. In Genesis 3:15, He gave the first hint of the One who would someday defeat Satan and provide hope for fallen, sinful man. Jesus Christ's heel would be bruised; He would die on the cross but rise from the grave—*alive!* And Satan's head would be crushed; he would eventually be defeated, never to rise to power again—*dead!*

In Genesis 3:21, God symbolically pictured salvation for Adam and Eve. Explain what He did.

What has been the most insightful thought for you in this chapter?

MEMORY VERSE

I will establish My covenant between Me and you and your descendants after you.

GENESIS 17:7

GENESIS
[The Book of Beginnings]

INSIGHT
Canaan was the most
backward and depraved
of the three major
civilizations of
Abraham's day.

DAY THREE

COMPLETE READ: Chapters 22--31
QUICK READ: Chapters 12:1-9; 13:14-18; 15:12-21; 17:1-8

A PROMINENT PLAYER

Picture this: A family is deeply rooted in their culture and community. All their relatives live close by, a pattern that has been followed for generations. They are happy and successful, honored and respected by their neighbors. Contentment and security is all they know. Then one day, the husband and father announces that the family will pull up stakes and move. The family is shocked! One family member after another legitimately asks, "Where are we going? Why are we moving?" But all the father can say is, "I don't know."

Seems a bit strange and insensitive and perhaps even stupid. But that's just what happened about four thousand years ago. The man was Abram; his wife was Sarai. Their story is recorded in Genesis 12:1-9 and expanded a bit in Acts 7:2-5. Read these two passages and describe how this move occurred.

Faith is a living, daring confidence in God's grace, so sure and certain that a man could stake his life on it a thousand times.

—MARTIN LUTHER, sixteenth-century German reformer

When Abram left Ur he left a 2000 BC lap of luxury. The city's population numbered 250,000. Its culture was extremely advanced in the arts and sciences: They'd been writing for over 1,000 years! Its standard of living was high, with the average middle-class home having 10 to 20 rooms and well over 2,000 square feet.[4] To leave this life to go who knows where says much about Abram. And his obedience to and faith in God proved to be the hallmark of his life.

The call of Abram by God is a watershed event not only in the book of Genesis but in the history of mankind. God made a covenant, an agreement, with this man that is still playing out today — and will continue to do so until the final curtain of history. There is no question that Abraham is a Prominent Player!

This covenant is detailed for us in Genesis 12:1-3. The agreement included three major components:

1. God chose one man, Abram, whom He promised to bless and make great.

2. From this one man, God would make a great nation, Israel. Those who bless Israel will be blessed; those who curse Israel will be cursed.

3. Through Abram and his seed, God would bless all the families of the earth.

God restated the covenant to Abram a number of times, each time adding a little more information. Briefly investigate the following passages and list the specifics each one adds to the covenant.

Genesis 13:14-18

Genesis 15:12-21 (especially verses 18-21)

Genesis 17:1-8

The original covenant indicated that all the families of the earth would be blessed through Abraham and his descendants (his "seed").

NOTE
An eclipse of the sun was observed by the Chinese seventy years before Abraham was born.

God is the God of promise. He keeps His word, even when that seems impossible; even when the circumstances seem to point to the opposite.

—Colin Urquhart, pastor

Compare Genesis 15:5 and 17:7 with Galatians 3:13-16. What is Paul's ultimate conclusion about the blessing of Abraham on all the families (Gentiles) of the earth?

God's covenant with Abraham has endured for over four thousand years! As promised, Abraham *was* blessed and his name *did* become great. In fact, three major religions of the world — Islam, Judaism, and Christianity — hold him in high esteem. As promised, God built a great nation, Israel, as his posterity. As promised, the families of the earth are *still* being blessed through his descendant, Jesus Christ — the Son of God, the Savior of the world, the One who provides the way back to God after the devastating results of sin in Genesis 3.

Describe your experience in being blessed as a result of this covenant with Abraham.

REVIEW IT!
Abraham is a Prominent Player because God chose him to be the father of the nation that would bring blessing to all the families of the world.

MEMORY VERSE

I will establish My covenant between Me and you and your descendants after you.

GENESIS 17:7

GENESIS
[The Book of Beginnings]

DAY FOUR

COMPLETE READ: Chapters 32--41
QUICK READ: Chapter 38

A NOTABLE FEATURE

Henry Vaughn writes,

> And here in dust and dirt, O here
> The lilies of His love appear.[5]

The Quick Read for today most likely left you feeling as if you were wandering in dust and dirt. The chapter appears to be simply a gross portrayal of sin—and for what? It's not the kind of passage you would choose for early morning reflection. But it is in the Bible—and for good reason. And that reason leads to our Notable Feature of the book of Genesis.

When we think of God's people, Israel, and the geographical places associated with them, we think of Canaan, Palestine, Israel, and Judah. But we don't want to overlook another place significant in the building of Israel as a nation (the second part of the covenant we studied yesterday).

Begin by reading Genesis 15:12-16. This is one of the restatements of the covenant by God to Abraham. As you read, answer the following questions.

What land is God talking about in verse 13? (Hint: What land will Moses lead the people out of?)

WOW!
Egypt was so advanced that the pyramids were built six hundred years before Abraham lived.

Have courage for the great sorrows of life and patience for the small ones; and when you have laboriously accomplished your daily task, go to sleep in peace. God is awake.

—VICTOR HUGO,
nineteenth-century writer

Summarize the flow of what will happen to Abraham's descendants. (Amorites is another name for Canaanites.)

In Abraham's day, God declared that His people would be subjected to slavery in Egypt for about four centuries. Isn't it logical to ask, "Why?" If they were in the land of promise during Abraham's time and that was the land God intended them to have forever, why go to the trouble of this four-hundred-year hiatus? This is where the "dust and dirt" of chapter 38 comes into play. For God's people to be a blessing to all the families of the earth, they needed to remain holy, pure, unique, and separate from the nations to whom they would be a blessing. Recall Abraham's desire and plan for Isaac not to marry a Canaanite woman (Genesis 24:1-4).

With that in mind, what does chapter 38 tell us about Judah, a great-grandson of Abraham and a representative of the people God was building into a nation to bless the earth? What does it show us about the Canaanites?

We've got double trouble here. God's people (illustrated in Judah) were being drawn to the Canaanite culture and lifestyle, and the Canaanites were gladly accepting and assimilating them. Chapter 38 shows us why God needed to remove His people from Canaan while He developed them into a great nation. But why did He choose Egypt?

Genesis 43:32 gives us significant insight. Joseph, who had been sold into slavery by his brothers, was now second in command in Egypt. A worldwide famine was in progress and his brothers had come to Egypt to buy grain, unaware that it was Joseph they were dealing with. Read Genesis 43:26-32. What does verse 32 say about Egypt that explains why God chose it?

Being a segregationist culture, Egypt was the perfect place for God to forge a separate and distinct people. Unlike Canaan, Egypt would allow God's people to be (in New Testament terms) "in the world, but not of the world." In the dust and dirt of chapter 38, God in His sovereignty caused the lilies of His love to appear. Judah's life began to change from that moment on, and soon Jacob's entire family was on their way to safety in Egypt. God showed that in the midst of sin, He still works for His glory and for His people's good.

Recall a time in your life when it was obvious that in the dust and dirt, the lilies of God's love appeared.

MEMORY VERSE

 I will establish My covenant between Me and you and your descendants after you.

GENESIS 17:7

REVIEW IT!
The Notable Feature of the book is God's sovereignty in choosing Egypt as the place to develop His nation.

GENESIS
[The Book of Beginnings]

JUST A THOUGHT
Joseph's "coat of many colors" was probably white, possibly with colored fringe.

DAY FIVE

COMPLETE READ: Chapters 42–50
QUICK READ: Chapter 22

A TIMELESS PRINCIPLE

After a long day at work, the young man simply wanted to go home and relax. But on his way to the elevator he heard screaming and saw smoke and flames billowing from the hallway. Panic gripped him: "I'm on the sixth floor. I'll never make it down." The hallway was engulfed in flames, but he remembered the windows in his office. When he reached them he could see nothing but smoke. He heard people yelling for him to jump, but fear smothered him. Over a loudspeaker a fireman shouted, "The only way you'll survive is to jump. We've spread a net; you'll be safe." But his courage fled. He couldn't see the net. Then he heard another voice: "It's okay son, you can jump." It was his dad—and his fear vanished. The relationship of love they had built over the years gave him the courage to trust his dad for what he could not see.[6]

Trust. Faith. It's not a leap into the unknown, not a shot in the dark, not a hope-so attitude. Rather, it's "the assurance of things hoped for, the conviction of things not seen" (Hebrews 11:1). It's certainly a Timeless Principle—and graphically displayed in the life of Abraham in Genesis 22.

By the time we reach Genesis 22, Isaac is a teenager. But Abraham had waited twenty-five years for this promised son to be born! And for most of those twenty-five years God had been silent. It is not difficult to imagine what Abraham felt for that son once he finally arrived. Deep love, intense pride, unspeakable delight, and

I do not want merely to possess a faith; I want a faith that possesses me.

—CHARLES KINGSLEY, nineteenth-century British writer

fatherly protection must have ruled his heart. And then he was faced with the devastating words of chapter 22, the supreme test of Abraham's life.

Read Genesis 22:1-2. If you were Abraham, what would you feel at this point?

THINK ABOUT IT
God gave language to man to bring order. At the Tower of Babel, God used that same gift to bring disorder.

Did you notice that God answered five of the six basic questions?

Who?

> *Your son, your only son, Isaac.*

When?

> *Now.*

Where?

> *The land of Moriah on a mountain I will show you.*

What?

> *Sacrifice him.*

How?

> *As a burnt offering.*

Why?

Belief is a truth held in the mind, faith is a fire in the heart.
—JOSEPH NEWTON, twentieth-century Baptist minister

No reason given. Just the command to go.

REMEMBER
Faith is the Timeless
Principle pictured
clearly in God's
command to Abraham
to sacrifice Isaac.

Read Genesis 22:3-7. What would have been going through your mind after Isaac asked a question like that?

Read Genesis 22:8 and compare it with Hebrews 11:17-19. What do these verses say about Abraham? Was this an easy task for him?

Read Genesis 22:9-12. Finally, the "why" question was answered. It's in verse 12. In your own words, describe that answer.

A. W. Tozer, in his book *Pursuit of God*, writes,

> God let the suffering old man go through with it up to the point where He knew there would be no retreat, and then forbade him to lay a hand upon the boy. To the wondering patriarch He now says in effect, "It's all right, Abraham. I never intended that you should actually slay the lad. I only wanted to remove him from the temple of your heart that I might reign unchallenged there. . . . Now I know that thou fearest God, seeing that thou hast not withheld thy son, thine only son, from me."[7]

Trust. Faith. Taking God at His word. But remember, this isn't trust and faith in a principle — it's trust and faith in a person, God Himself. It's about trusting the love relationship with a Father who says it's okay to jump.

Quickly scan the following verses again, emphasizing the words *God*, *He*, and *Lord* as they appear: Genesis 22:1-3,8-12.

The more we depend
on God the more
dependable we find
He is.

—CLIFF RICHARD

Describe a time when you trusted God in a very difficult situation.

What were the challenges?

What do you think enabled you to trust Him?

How are you different because of the experience?

MEMORY VERSE

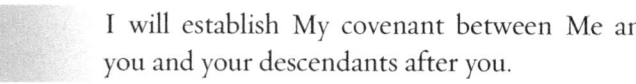
I will establish My covenant between Me and you and your descendants after you.

GENESIS 17:7

May there fall upon me now, O God, a great sense of Thy power and Thy glory, so that I may see all earthly things in their true measure. I am content, O Father, to leave my life in Thy hands. I am content to give over my will to Thy control.

—JOHN BAILLIE,
A Diary of Private Prayer

GENESIS
[The Book of Beginnings]

REVIEW

1. The theme of Genesis is the book of _____.

2. Chapter 3 is a Crucial Chapter in its description of man's first sin and God's first promise of _____.

3. _____ is a Prominent Player because God chose him to be the father of the nation that would bring blessing to all the families of the world.

4. The Notable Feature of the book is God's _____ in choosing Egypt as the place to develop His nation.

5. "I will establish My _____ between Me and you and your descendants after you."

GENESIS 17: _____

EXODUS

[The Book of Deliverance]

I am the LORD *your God, who brought you out of*

the land of Egypt, out of the house of slavery.

EXODUS 20:2

EXODUS
[The Book of Deliverance]

INTRODUCTION

The book of Exodus continues the story of Abraham's family. His descendants, the Israelites, had grown from a family of seventy to over two million people. While they were living in the land of Goshen, an area within the country of Egypt, the political climate changed and the Israelites were forced to live in slavery.

Yet God heard their cries for help and raised up a leader, Moses, to lead the people to freedom. In one of the most amazing series of miracles in the Bible, God delivered His people from cruel bondage into liberty. God led them out of Egypt, across the Red Sea, and to Mount Sinai. There He gave them the Ten Commandments and the instructions to build the tabernacle, an elaborate portable tent where the glory of God dwelt among His chosen people.

Most of Exodus covers a period of less than two years. In that short time, God revealed much about His character, His awesome power, and His faithfulness to keep His promises. It is this same God who offers liberty to you today.

Exodus
[The Book of Deliverance]

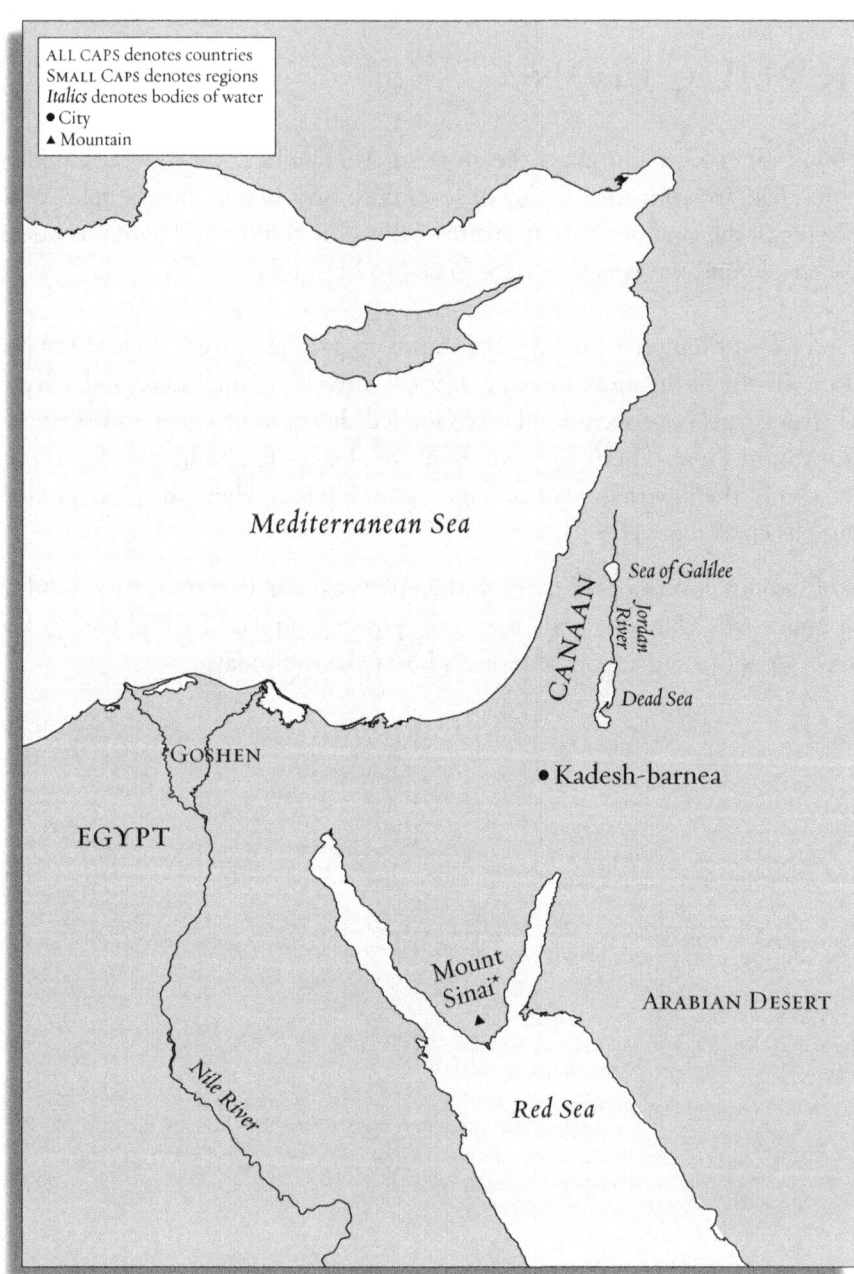

ALL CAPS denotes countries
SMALL CAPS denotes regions
Italics denotes bodies of water
● City
▲ Mountain

Mediterranean Sea

CANAAN

Sea of Galilee

Jordan River

Dead Sea

GOSHEN

● Kadesh-barnea

EGYPT

Mount Sinai*
▲

ARABIAN DESERT

Nile River

Red Sea

*The actual location of Mount Sinai is believed to be here though it is still a matter of debate.

EXODUS
[The Book of Deliverance]

OVERVIEW

WHO: Author: Moses
Main Character: Moses

WHAT: You shall have no other gods before Me

WHEN: The book covers approximately 400 years, though the majority of the book spans less than 2 years. Chapters 7–40 span about 1 year—around 1445 BC

WHERE: The book begins in Egypt and ends at Mount Sinai

WHY: God delivers the Israelites out of Egyptian bondage

I. GOD _____ ISRAEL FROM EGYPTIAN BONDAGE (EXODUS 1–14).

    A. God appointed _____ to deliver the people (Exodus 3–4).

    B. God sent ten _____ upon the Egyptians (Exodus 7–11).

    C. _____ is the celebration of God passing over the Israelites when He brought death to all the firstborn children of Egypt (Exodus 12).

    D. God parted the _____ and brought the Israelites out of Egypt (Exodus 14).

II. THE ISRAELITES GRUMBLED AND _____ WHEN THEY REFUSED TO TRUST GOD (EXODUS 15–18).

    A. They were afraid they would starve and God sent quail and

    _____.

    B. They were afraid they would die of thirst and God sent _____ from a rock.

    C. Moses needed help and God sent _____.

III. At Mount Sinai, God declared His plan for Israel (Exodus 19–24).

    A. The Ten _____ gave order to life.

        1. The first four commandments dealt with man's relationship to God.

            a. Have no other gods.

            b. Do not make for yourself an idol.

            c. Do not take the Lord's name in vain.

            d. Honor the Sabbath Day and keep it holy.

        2. The next six commandments dealt with man's relationship to man.

            a. Honor your mother and your father.

            b. Do not murder.

            c. Do not commit adultery.

            d. Do not steal.

            e. Do not bear false witness against your neighbor.

            f. Do not covet.

IV. God gave instructions for the people to build the tabernacle (Exodus 25–40).

    A. They built the tabernacle to God's instructions.

    B. At the end of Exodus, the glory of the Lord filled the tabernacle (Exodus 40:34).

    C. The tabernacle was a constant reminder that God lived among them.

Application

God has the power to deliver us from bondage and bring us into the joy of His presence, provision, and protection.

EXODUS
[The Book of Deliverance]

LEARNING FOR LIFE

1. Beginning in Genesis, build the foundation for the book of Exodus (group effort).

2. Read Genesis 15:13-16. God gave a promise to Abraham.

   a. What part does the book of Exodus play in that promise?

   b. What does this say about God's faithfulness?

3. If you were part of the Exodus, at what point would you be totally convinced that God was indeed the only all-wise, all-powerful God?

4. The night the death angel passed over the homes of the Israelites was a pivotal point in Israel's history. How is Christ connected to the Passover? (See 1 Corinthians 5:7; 1 Peter 1:18-19.)

5. There are Ten Commandments (Exodus 20). Review them and tell why you think God chose each one for His people.

6. Exodus is a book about people held in bondage and an awesome God who delivered them to freedom. What are some of the things that hold us in bondage today?

EXODUS
[The Book of Deliverance]

FACT
The Israelites enjoyed seventy-five years of prosperity and peace in Egypt following Joseph's death and prior to Exodus 1:8.

DAY ONE

COMPLETE READ: Chapters 1--10
QUICK READ: Chapter 1

THE BIG PICTURE

When Jacob and his family entered Egypt, they numbered 70 (see Genesis 46:27). When they left 400 years later, they numbered approximately 2.5 million! Even if they were well-behaved, which they weren't, can you imagine leading that kind of multitude? Consider these statistics:

- Assuming one family needed a 50 foot by 50 foot area in which to pitch their tent and bed down their livestock (most likely 6 per family), the multitude would need 3 billion square feet — 10.5 miles by 10.5 miles.

- When the throng approached the Red Sea, marching 50 abreast (people and animals), their column would have stretched back 123 miles.

- If you watched this incredible parade pass at the speed of 2.5 miles per hour, you would have to stand there for 49 hours.

- If God had chosen to bring manna for the people and food for the animals by rail, the train would have numbered 160 boxcars *every day.*

- If a person drank a minimal 1 gallon of water per day and an animal 2 gallons per day, they would have needed another 1,080 tank cars.

- The train, now 1,240 cars, would have stretched 9.5 miles from engine to caboose.[1]

All great changes are irksome to the human mind, especially those which are attended with great dangers and uncertain effects.

—JOHN ADAMS, second U.S. president

God's provision for His people — *for 40 years* — was nothing short of miraculous. And Moses' leadership of this incredible undertaking was, to say the least, impressive.

The story of exiting Egypt and entering Canaan begins in the book of Exodus. By the end of the book the people are still many miles and 39 years from settling in the land of promise, but the epic journey has begun.

The information in the book of Exodus can be summarized as follows:

1 14	15 18	19 40
DELIVERANCE by God from Egypt	**DISCONTENT of the** People in the Wilderness	**DECLARATIONS** by God at Mount Sinai
Bondage	Quail	Ten Commandments
Moses	Manna	Various Other Laws
Plagues	Water	Golden Calf
Red Sea	Jethro	Tabernacle

As you can see from the chart, many familiar and significant events take place in the book of Exodus. We will touch on some of them over the next few days.

As with the other books of the Pentateuch, Moses is the author. Assuming Moses wrote this record soon after leaving Egypt, we can estimate the date. First Kings 6:1 states that "in the four hundred and eightieth year after the sons of Israel came out of the land of Egypt" Solomon began to build the temple of the Lord. Through archaeological records we are able to trace that event to 960 BC. Therefore, 480 years earlier in 1440 BC, the Exodus occurred and Moses began to record the events preserved for us in this book.

God's prophecy spoken to Abram 640 years earlier had come true: "God said to Abram, 'Know for certain that your descendants will be strangers in a land that is not theirs, where they will be enslaved and oppressed four hundred years'" (Genesis 15:13). A long and trying time for the Israelites had indeed come to pass.

DID YOU KNOW? The plagues lasted a total of about six months.

This is a sane, wholesome, practical, working faith: first, that it is a man's business to do the will of God; second, that God takes on Himself the special care of that man; and third, that therefore that man ought never to be afraid of anything.

—GEORGE MACDONALD, nineteenth-century Scottish novelist and poet

But now the good part of the prophecy is about to be fulfilled: "But I will also judge the nation whom they will serve, and afterward they will come out with many possessions" (Genesis 15:14). That coming out "with many possessions" is the drama of Exodus—a drama that pits the strength of Jehovah against the strength of Egypt, its gods, and its Pharaoh. And in that drama God says, "You shall have no other gods before Me."

Your Quick Read for today links the books of Genesis and Exodus. Write down the major ideas from the chapter. Then pray, asking God to make your heart responsive to the truths you will see in Exodus.

MEMORY VERSE

I am the LORD your God, who brought you out of the land of Egypt, out of the house of slavery.

EXODUS 20:2

EXODUS
[The Book of Deliverance]

DAY TWO

COMPLETE READ: Chapters 10--20
QUICK READ: Chapters 11--12

DID YOU KNOW?
The Passover month,
April, became the first
month of the year
for the Israelites
(Exodus 12:2).

CRUCIAL CHAPTERS

Defining Moment: a point or period of time when things are forever changed. It is no longer business as usual — the status quo is abolished, the past is no more, and a new future arrives.

A marriage ceremony. The birth of a child. The death of a loved one.

The Declaration of Independence. The last spike driven in the Transcontinental Railroad. The passing of the nineteenth amendment, assuring a woman's right to vote. 9/11.

Sometimes an event's significance is immediate; at other times only hindsight offers a clear understanding. And often it's a little of both.

The Passover was just such a defining moment — part of its significance immediately apparent and part of its significance revealed over time. The chapters containing its original enactment are our Crucial Chapters and your Quick Read for today.

The original significance of the Passover was the protection of the Israelites' lives by God during the tenth and final plague on Egypt. It was this plague that finally broke the back of Pharaoh's resistance and paved the way for God's people to leave Egypt and begin their trek to the Promised Land.

Our moments of inspiration are not lost though we have no particular poem to show for them; for those experiences have left an indelible impression, and we are ever and anon reminded of them.
—HENRY DAVID THOREAU, American writer

The Lamb of the
Passover was to be
killed between 3 and 6
PM, the same time the
Lamb of God died—
1,450 years later.

Read Exodus 11:4-7 and describe the plague in your own words.

After reading Exodus 12:1-13, describe in two or three sentences how the Israelites were to prepare in order to be spared from the plague of the death of all firstborns.

Look at the following summary of Passover instructions. It will help you grasp the individual components of the action required of the Israelites.

If there be ground for you to trust in your own righteousness, then all that Christ did to purchase salvation, and all that God did to prepare the way for it, is in vain.

—Jonathan Edwards, eighteenth-century Puritan writer and preacher

SELECTION of the Lamb		SLAYING of the Lamb		SUPPER of the Lamb	
Key: **PERFECTION**		Key: **PROTECTION**		Key: **PROVISION**	
To be proven unblemished		To be painted on doorposts		To be eaten the same night	
12:3	12:6	12:6	12:7	12:8	12:11

The perfection was to be proven by selecting a lamb on the tenth of the month and observing it until the fourteenth. The protection would occur as a result of painting the lamb's blood on the lintel and doorposts, going into the house, and not coming out until morning. The provision would take place as the Israelites ate the lamb according to the thirteen stipulations in Exodus 12:8-11.

If the people followed these instructions, they could be confident of protection from the plague. According to Exodus 12:12-13,23, who would carry out the plague and what would withhold the plague's destruction from Israelite homes?

DID YOU KNOW?
Pharaoh's daughter, the Egyptian woman who raised Moses, was probably a daughter by one of his concubines, not a princess of royal blood.

Read Exodus 12:24-27,42 and describe the significance and intention of this event.

This entire event is a clear foreshadowing of the eventual death of the Lamb of God — God's Son, Jesus Christ.

- He was selected before the foundations of the world by His Father and proven during His thirty-plus years on earth to be perfect.

- He was slain for the protection of those who would receive the application of His blood to their lives, thus avoiding God's wrath.

- He is the supper — the provision of sustenance for those who have avoided the wrath of God.

The Passover was the historical event that saved God's people in Egypt from the death of their firstborn and caused Pharaoh to let them go free. Down through the centuries, Jews have celebrated

Salvation is the work of God for man; it is not the work of man for God.
—LEWIS SPERRY CHAFER, American Bible teacher, evangelist, educator, and writer

Passover as a feast of remembrance of this defining moment in their history. For Christians, it foreshadows the event on which our eternity hangs — the death of Jesus Christ, of whom the apostle Paul said in 1 Corinthians 5:7, "For Christ our Passover also has been sacrificed."

Where do you stand in relation to the Passover Lamb? Are you protected by His blood from God's wrath against sin? If not, you can be. Talk to God and confess your sins. Ask His forgiveness and by faith accept His gift of protection. If you are a Christ-follower, thank God now for the work of the Passover Lamb in your life.

The Lord is loving unto man, and swift to pardon, but slow to punish. Let no man therefore despair of his own salvation.

—SAINT CYRIL OF JERUSALEM, first-century bishop

REVIEW IT!
Chapters 11 and 12 are Crucial Chapters because they show us how the Passover is a defining moment in God's plan to bring salvation to Israel and the world.

MEMORY VERSE

I am the LORD your God, who brought you out of the land of Egypt, out of the house of slavery.

EXODUS 20:2

EXODUS
[The Book of Deliverance]

DAY THREE

COMPLETE READ: Chapters 21–27
QUICK READ: Chapters 3:1–4:17

INTERESTING!
Moses worked as a
shepherd in the same
region where he would
eventually lead the
Israelites.

A PROMINENT PLAYER

It was 1934 in Europe and Hitler's anti-Semitism was sweeping a continent. Heinz was an eleven-year-old Jew when the streets of his Bavarian village became a battleground overrun by Hitler's thugs. To avoid trouble, Heinz learned to keep his eyes open. But one day, he couldn't avoid the thugs and a beating seemed inevitable. Yet he walked away unhurt — not because he fought back, but because he spoke up. He used words to dispel conflict. He found many more opportunities to hone the skill that would one day define him. Eventually, his family escaped from Bavaria to America. Later in life, his name became synonymous with negotiations of peace. His name was Henry Kissinger.[2]

As a young boy, Heinz was already becoming what he would one day be. And the same was true of Moses, our Prominent Player. We think of him mostly as the deliverer of Israel. But that was only one-third of his life. Take away the other two-thirds, and he never would have become the great leader God called him to be.

Remember the story of Moses in the bulrushes (Exodus 2:1-10)? He eventually was raised and trained as the son of Pharaoh's daughter. What do you think his experience at the top of Egyptian society for forty years built into him?

*Now I become myself.
It's taken time, many
years and places.*

—MAY SARTON, poet

Now read Exodus 2:11-15. This event occurred when Moses was about forty years old. What do you think this experience added to his understanding of himself and life?

THINK ABOUT IT
Moses, the future deliverer of Israel, was himself miraculously delivered as an infant.

Moses then married a Midianite girl and became a shepherd of her father's flocks (Exodus 3:1). In no time at all, he went from being a somebody among somebodies to a nobody among nobodies. From prince in the palace to shepherd in the wilderness. From commanding thousands of obedient servants to overseeing dumb sheep. From answering to Pharaoh, the king, to answering to Jethro, his father-in-law. Talk about a mid-life crisis! And he lived this way for forty years.

What do you think these forty years taught him about becoming what he would be?

Our mundane experiences contain all the stuff of holiness and of human growth in grace. But so much goes unnoticed. We are too busy to name the event that is blessed in its ordinariness, holy in its uniqueness, and grace-filled in its underlying challenge.
—JOAN PULS,
Every Bush Is Burning

And then at age eighty, everything changed. Edmund Burke, the eighteenth-century political philosopher, penned the phrase, "History is full of momentous trifles."[3] Ordinary events can be pierced with extraordinary meaning. Moses' day was ordinary; he was just shepherding the sheep like any and every other day (Exodus 3:1). But God was about to make this trifling day momentous. Then there was the bush — an ordinary, trifling little bush. But God was about to make it momentous. It was on fire, but it wasn't burning up. Then God spoke to Moses from the middle of the bush. At that instant, Moses' life drastically changed.

Summarize the Quick Read for today (Exodus 3:1–4:17). Try to capture Moses' struggle with God and God's call on Moses' life.

WOW!
Each of the ten plagues was a judgment against a specific Egyptian god.

Eventually, Moses and his brother Aaron challenged Pharaoh to let God's people go. God sent plagues to convince Pharaoh. The Israelites miraculously crossed the Red Sea, and the Egyptians were drowned in it. Exodus 14:30-31 records the epilogue to the phenomenal Red Sea experience. Read these verses and describe how the people felt about Moses.

Obviously, there is a lot more to come in the story of Moses' leadership of the people. But up to this point, summarize three or four thoughts you have had about how God worked with Moses while he was in the process of becoming what he would be.

It's not a plan we create that determines our fulfillment. It's what we let God do in the plan of His choosing.

—GLAPHRE GILLILAND, author and teacher

How do you think God has worked in your life as you've gone through the process of becoming what you will be?

REVIEW IT!
Moses is the Prominent Player in Exodus as God works with him to help him become what he needs to be.

MEMORY VERSE

I am the LORD your God, who brought you out of the land of Egypt, out of the house of slavery.

EXODUS 20:2

Exodus
[The Book of Deliverance]

DAY FOUR

COMPLETE READ: Chapters 28–31
QUICK READ: Chapter 40

FACT
The tabernacle
courtyard covered
approximately a quarter
of an acre.

A NOTABLE FEATURE

Scarlet Material	Purple Linen	Bronze	Gold
Setting Stones	Onyx Stones	Silver	Hooks
Fine Twisted Linen	Curtains	Sockets	Pegs
Ram's Skin Dyed Red	Goat's Hair	Spices	Bars
Porpoise Skins	Blue Veil	Boards	Oil
Acacia Wood	Utensils	Poles	

As the list above indicates, the instructions given for the building of the tabernacle included detail after detail regarding materials and products to be made from materials. The dimensions of specific parts of the tabernacle were also given with explicit precision: thirty cubits; a cubit long and a cubit wide; two cubits high; ten by ten by ten cubits; a hand breadth all around; and on and on. Everything was to be just so: the right color, the right size, the right fabric, the right number.

Why the detail? Why the perfection—dare we say *pickiness?* Because it was for God, and it was to be His place to dwell among the people—His home. And all this beauty and precision demanded portability because God knew the Israelites would be pitching and breaking camp over and over for forty years! It also had to be *just so* because in addition to being the place where God would live, it would also be the place from where He would display His awesome radiance to His people.

Jesus is not one of many ways to approach God, nor is He the best of several ways; He is the only way.
—A. W. TOZER,
twentieth-century
author and theologian

And there was still another reason it had to be *just so*—it would provide a way for sinful people to approach a holy God. It would be the way to secure forgiveness of sin and to enjoy fellowship in His presence.

To get a feel for the instructions received, read these two brief passages: Exodus 36:20-34, which describes work for the tabernacle, and Exodus 37:17-24, which describes how to make the lampstands for inside the tabernacle. Jot down a few words to describe your impressions of what you've read.

The diagram that follows indicates the layout of the tabernacle, including its rooms and its furniture.

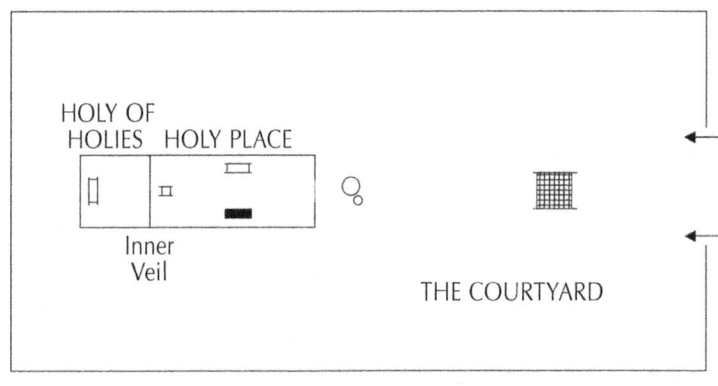

HOLY OF HOLIES   HOLY PLACE

Inner Veil

THE COURTYARD

TABERNACLE KEY

Brazen Altar

Bronze Laver

Table of Showbread

Golden Lampstand

Altar of Incense

Ark of the Covenant

The next chart briefly describes the function of each piece of furniture. We'll see more detail about this in the book of Leviticus.

FURNITURE	LOCATION	FUNCTION
Brazen Altar	Courtyard	Place to perform various sacrifices
Bronze Laver	Courtyard	Place for daily cleansing of the priests
Table of Showbread	Holy Place	Once a week the priests ate the bread
Golden Lampstand	Holy Place	Provided light in the Holy Place
Altar of Incense	Holy Place	Twice a day incense was burned to God
Inner Veil	Between Holy Place and Holy of Holies	Separated man from God; high priest entered through it once a year
Ark of the Covenant	Holy of Holies	Held mercy seat and indicated presence of God
Mercy Seat	Holy of Holies	The lid of the ark; blood was sprinkled there once a year for forgiveness

Every piece of furniture and every function pointed to Jesus Christ. This earthly tabernacle was the Israelites' realization of the presence and glory of God and their way of approach to God. So too, Jesus Christ is our realization of the presence and glory of God and our way of approach to God. Read John 1:14, realizing that the phrase "dwelt among us" literally means "tabernacled among us."

Think about the pieces of furniture and explain in your own words how Jesus Christ fulfilled these pictures represented in the tabernacle.

I have a great need for Christ; I have a great Christ for my need.

—CHARLES SPURGEON, nineteenth-century British preacher

Read Exodus 40:34-38. If you were an Israelite watching this scene in person, what would you think? What would you feel?

MEMORY VERSE

I am the LORD your God, who brought you out of the land of Egypt, out of the house of slavery.

EXODUS 20:2

EXODUS
[The Book of Deliverance]

DAY FIVE

DID YOU KNOW?
The third
commandment means
we are not to use
God's name lightly or
flippantly.

COMPLETE READ: Chapters 32–40
QUICK READ: Chapter 20

A TIMELESS PRINCIPLE

In his book *The Ten(der) Commandments*, Ron Mehl tells a story of the famous golfer Chi Chi Rodriguez. The golfer was driving with a friend, and when the light changed to red he sped right through it. "Chi Chi!" his friend yelled. "You went right through a red light!" Chi Chi replied, "My brother taught me to drive and he doesn't stop for red lights, so neither do I." Sure enough, at the next red light — zoom, he went right through it. His friend was a nervous wreck, but Chi Chi just repeated, "My brother taught me to drive and he doesn't stop for red lights, so neither do I." They soon came to a green light and Chi Chi stopped, nervously looking both ways. "Why are you stopping *now* at this green light?" his friend asked. Chi Chi replied, "My brother might be coming!"[4]

All of us run red lights from time to time. Maybe not the physical type hanging above the intersection, but certainly the moral type hanging above our consciences. Our Timeless Principle, or more accurately Principles, is a series of red lights given to us by God. Many prefer to call them the Ten Suggestions, but God calls them the Ten Commandments. They are found in Exodus 20:1-21 and can best be remembered as two major sections, each with a different focus.

The Ten Commandments are God's righteous will for His people, given not as a club over our heads but as a tug on our hearts. He gives them not to frustrate us but to free us to live in harmony with holiness.

We may not all break the Ten Commandments, but we are certainly all capable of it. Within us lurks the breaker of all laws, ready to spring out at the first real opportunity.

—ISADORA DUNCAN, twentieth-century ballerina

COMMANDMENTS I–IV	COMMANDMENTS V–X
I. Do not have other gods before Me. II. Do not make idols to worship. III. Do not use God's name lightly. IV. Keep the Sabbath day holy.	V. Honor your father and mother. VI. Do not murder. VII. Do not commit adultery. VIII. Do not steal. IX. Do not bear false witness. X. Do not covet.
Relationship to GOD	Relationship to MAN
You shall love the Lord your God with all your heart, soul, and mind (Matthew 22:37).	You shall love your neighbor as yourself (Matthew 22:39).

These commandments were part of Israel's constitution as a people. As with other constitutions, this one includes a preamble. Read Exodus 19:3-6 and write down the principles laid out in this preamble.

Now look at chapter 20. In verses 1-2 God succinctly states His motivation for giving the Ten Commandments and the people's motivation for following them. Describe and respond to each motivation.

God's motivation:

Somebody figured it out—we have 35 million laws trying to enforce Ten Commandments.

—EARL WILSON, twentieth-century American author and columnist

The people's motivation:

As you read through these commandments, which ones do you think are more consistently disobeyed than others? Why?

DID YOU KNOW?
In form, the Ten Commandments follow the pattern of Near Eastern treaties of the thirteenth-century BC.

In your walk with God, you have probably noticed that the Law does a much better job of pointing out your sin than empowering you to overcome your sin. If that is your experience, you are right on course. The Law is designed to show us our sin (see Romans 7:7) and lead us in complete dependence to the only One who has ever obeyed the Law perfectly — Jesus Christ (see Romans 5:17-21; 8:1-4). A personal relationship with Him frees us from the penalty of breaking God's law and empowers us to live out the provisions of that Law.

With those thoughts as a foundation, which commandment has historically been most challenging for you? Why?

The beginning and the end of the law is kindness.
—Jewish proverb

What progress have you seen in your life in this area? In other words, how are you different than you were ten years ago?

Remember, these commandments express God's righteous will for you and were given to you from a heart of love, deeply desiring your best. Is there something in these Timeless Principles that you need to address more seriously? If so, what? And what would more serious attention look like?

Am I willing to give up what I have in order to be what I am not yet? Am I able to follow the spirit of love into the desert? It is a frightening and sacred moment. There is no return. One's life is changed forever. It is the fire that gives us our shape.

—Mary Caroline Richards, twentieth-century teacher, writer, potter, and poet

MEMORY VERSE

I am the LORD your God, who brought you out of the land of Egypt, out of the house of slavery.

EXODUS 20:2

EXODUS
[The Book of Deliverance]

REVIEW

1. The theme of Exodus is you shall have no other _____ before Me.

2. Chapters 11 and 12 are Crucial Chapters because they show us how the _____ is a defining moment in God's plan to bring salvation to Israel and the world.

3. _____ is the Prominent Player in Exodus as God works with him to help him become what he needs to be.

4. The _____ is a Notable Feature of Exodus because it represents the presence of God and our way of approach to God.

5. "I am the LORD your God, who brought you out of the land of Egypt, out of the house of _____."

EXODUS 20: _____

LEVITICUS

[The Book of Holiness]

You shall be holy, for I am holy.

LEVITICUS 11:45

THREE

LEVITICUS
[The Book of Holiness]

INTRODUCTION

While the Israelites were camped at the foot of Mount Sinai, God gave them civil, moral, and religious laws. It was here that He showed them the proper way to approach a holy God. Sin had separated man from God, and the punishment for sin is death.

In Leviticus, however, God gave Israel a way out of that punishment. He provided them with detailed instructions regarding sacrifices and offerings so that unholy men and women could live in communion with a holy God. He allowed the death of animals to serve as a substitute payment for man's sin. This instructional book points toward the final sacrifice of Jesus Christ — the Messiah — who would come fourteen hundred years later.

LEVITICUS
[The Book of Holiness]

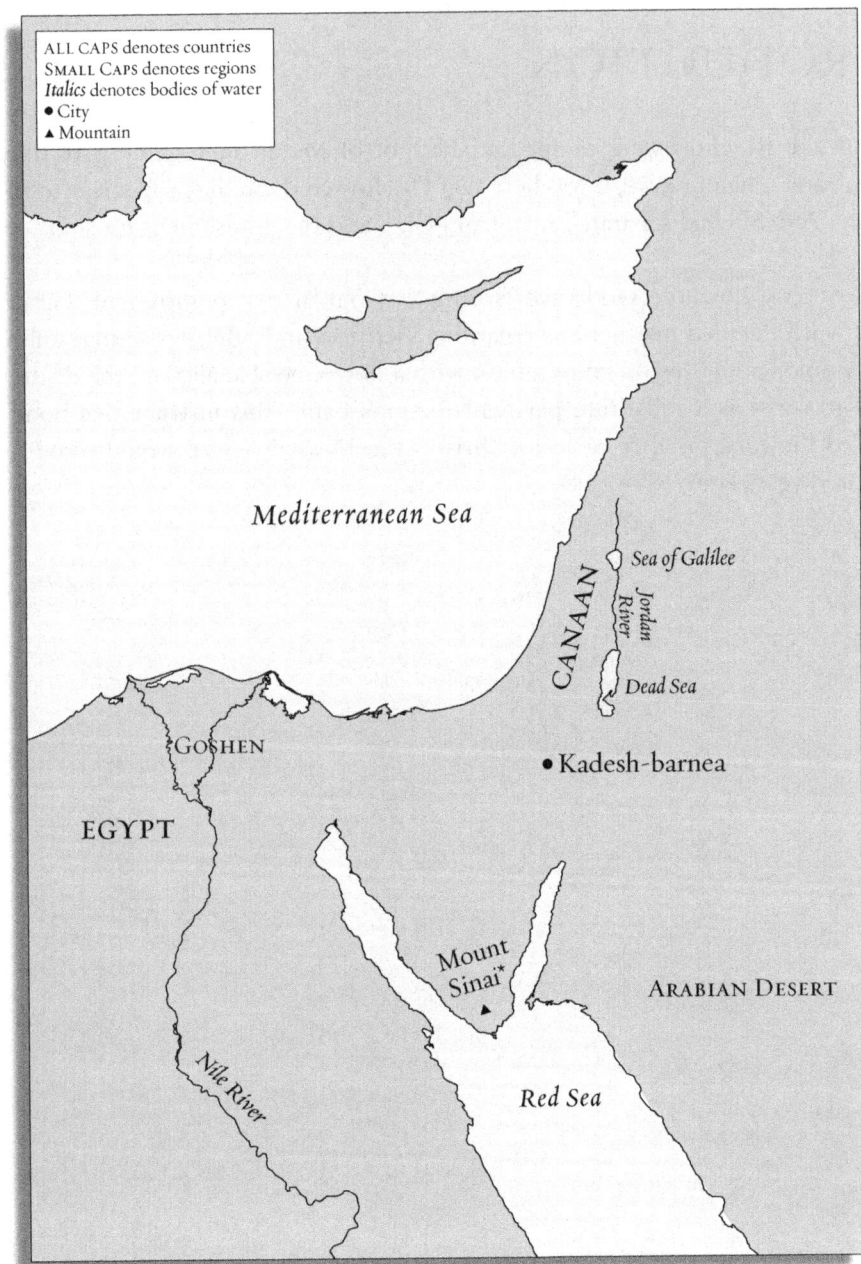

ALL CAPS denotes countries
SMALL CAPS denotes regions
Italics denotes bodies of water
● City
▲ Mountain

Mediterranean Sea

CANAAN

Sea of Galilee

Jordan River

Dead Sea

● Kadesh-barnea

GOSHEN

EGYPT

Mount Sinai*
▲

ARABIAN DESERT

Nile River

Red Sea

*The actual location of Mount Sinai is believed to be here though it is still a matter of debate.

L EVITICUS

[*The Book of Holiness*]

OVERVIEW

WHO: Author: Moses
          Main Characters: Moses and his brother Aaron
WHAT: You shall be holy, for I am holy
WHEN: Approximately one year after the Exodus. The book spans one month
WHERE: The entire book takes place at the foot of Mount Sinai
WHY: The book of Leviticus was Israel's guidebook to holiness

I. THE _____ : THE HOLY DWELLING OF GOD

   A. The brazen _____ was directly inside the east gate in the courtyard of the tabernacle.

      1. This altar represented the people's need for a blood sacrifice to approach God. Christ's sacrifice was the last sacrifice and is sufficient for us today.

   B. The bronze _____ came next in the courtyard.

      1. This represented the need for cleansing from sin before approaching God.

      2. Today, if we confess our sins, Christ is faithful to forgive us and cleanse us from our sins.

   C. The table of _____ held twelve loaves of bread and was inside the Holy Place on the north wall.

      1. This represented the twelve tribes of Israel.

      2. Jesus Christ is the Bread of Life.

   D. The _____ burned continually and was inside the Holy Place on the south wall.

      1. This represented Jesus Christ, the Light of the World.

   E. The altar of _____ was in the Holy Place on the west wall.

      1. This represented the prayers of the saints.

2. Christ is the intercessor of our prayers.

F. The _____ separated the Holy Place from the Most Holy place.

   1. This represented the barrier between man and God.

   2. At Christ's death the veil was torn in two from top to bottom. Now through Christ, there is no barrier between God and man.

G. The _____ of the covenant was in the Most Holy Place and contained the Ten Commandments. The lid was called the mercy seat and represented the mercy of Jesus Christ.

II. THE WAY TO GOD IS THROUGH SACRIFICE (LEVITICUS 1–16).

Leviticus 1–16 records instructions for the religious life of the Israelites, how the tabernacle was to be used, the duties of the priests, and the instructions for worship, celebration, and sacrifice.

A. The five types of sacrifice for the Israelites before Christ were:

Voluntary

   1. _____ offering

   2. _____ offering

   3. _____ offering

Compulsory

   4. _____ offering

   5. _____ offering

B. Today, Jesus is our sacrifice. John 14:6 says, "I am the way, and the truth, and the life; no one comes to the Father but through Me."

III. THE WALK WITH GOD DEMANDS HOLINESS (LEVITICUS 17–27).

Leviticus 17–27 records the laws for a life of holiness for the Israelites.

A. Leviticus 11:44 says, "Consecrate yourselves therefore, and be holy, for I am holy."

B. The concept of holiness appears eighty-four times in the book of Leviticus.

C. Leviticus 23 gives instructions for the holidays and feasts to celebrate so the Israelites would remember what God had done for them.

D. Israel was to be an example to other nations of the benefits and blessings of living a holy life in communion with a holy God.

APPLICATION

We are to be examples to those around us as we live in holiness and communion with God. People will see a difference in us if there is a difference to see.

LEVITICUS
[The Book of Holiness]

LEARNING FOR LIFE

1. Beginning in Genesis, build the foundation for Leviticus (group effort).

2. Why does God require a blood sacrifice?

3. Why do you think God wanted the people to be present at the death of the sacrificed animal?

    a. What difference would this make to you?

    b. What does this say about God's attitude toward sin?

4. Sacrifice is a recurring theme in Leviticus. Is there a New Testament connection to this theme? (See Hebrews 10:11-14.)

5. There are several feasts and celebrations in Leviticus. What do they reveal about God?

6. Do you take your sin as seriously as God does? Explain your answer.

LEVITICUS
[The Book of Holiness]

DAY ONE

COMPLETE READ: Chapters 1--5
QUICK READ: Chapter 1

THE BIG PICTURE

About AD 63 to 64, just a few years before his martyrdom during the persecutions of Nero, the apostle Peter wrote these words in 1 Peter 1:14-16: "As obedient children, do not be conformed to the former lusts which were yours in your ignorance, but like the Holy One who called you, be holy yourselves also in all your behavior; because it is written, 'YOU SHALL BE HOLY, FOR I AM HOLY.'"

In these verses, Peter quotes from what was at that time a 1,500-year-old book — the book of Leviticus. Today it is almost 3,500 years old, and because of its difficult subject matter, we are tempted to relegate its usefulness to antiquity. But if we read through Exodus, skip Leviticus, and go on to Numbers, we do so to our own detriment because its message is crucial to walking with God.

It's all about holiness — holiness in the *initial* sense of turning away from the ignorance of our previous conformity to lusts, and holiness in the ongoing *progressive* sense of continuously and consistently molding our behavior into God's image: "You shall be holy, for I am holy." That is the book of Leviticus.

The true Christian ideal is not to be happy but to be holy.
—A. W. TOZER, twentieth-century author and theologian

The following chart shows the Big Picture of the book.

CHAPTERS 1–16	CHAPTERS 17–27
How to APPROACH a Holy God	How to WALK with a Holy God
Emphasis: 5 Offerings	Emphasis: 7 Feasts
Sacrifice	Sanctification
"I am Holy"	"You shall be Holy"

At the end of the book of Exodus, the tabernacle was completed. With its completion, God had a particular place for His manifestation and presence, and the people had a place to approach their God. The book of Leviticus describes the inner workings of that place and the proper ways for people to approach God there.

The first section focuses on the sacrifices to be offered to God because "without shedding of blood there is no forgiveness" (Hebrews 9:22). The second section describes in more detail what it meant for God's people to be sanctified, to be holy. The word *sanctification* literally means "to be set apart, separated, unique." God's people were not to be like other people, but rather they were to be unique in their relationship to and behavior before their God. Who He was—holy and set apart—defined who they should be. The concept of holiness occurs eighty-seven times in the book. You can't miss it!

Leviticus does not provide any chronological movement. Its revelation was received over a period of approximately one month. As with the other books of the Pentateuch, Moses is its author. He recorded it most likely around 1440 BC and edited it prior to his death about forty years later.

As we will see, Leviticus prefigures Christ page after page. Much of the book of Hebrews would be obscure in its meaning without the book of Leviticus to refer to. Christ fulfills and completes the sacrifices, the feasts, and the priesthood described in this book.

Spend some time meditating on the memory verse for this week. How would you describe the holiness of God?

You must be holy in the way God asks you to be holy. God does not ask you to be a Trappist monk or a hermit. He wills that you sanctify the world and your everyday life.

—Vincent Pallotti, nineteenth-century Italian priest

Memory Verse

You shall be holy, for I am holy.

Leviticus 11:45

REVIEW IT! The theme of Leviticus is you shall be holy, for I am holy.

LEVITICUS
[The Book of Holiness]

INSIGHT
The word *atonement* is used forty-five times in the book of Leviticus.

DAY TWO

COMPLETE READ: Chapters 6–11
QUICK READ: Chapter 16

A CRUCIAL CHAPTER

The crime took place in a one-room mountain schoolhouse. The teacher was determined to discover who had taken Sally Jane's lunch when they all heard a sob. It was Billy — thin, undernourished, a poorest-of-the-poor child. "I was hungry," he explained through his tears. The teacher acknowledged Billy's need for food but insisted that punishment must be given. The teacher removed the leather strap from the wall as Billy went to the front of the room and removed his shirt. Just when the teacher was ready to inflict punishment, a husky voice from the rear of the room shouted, "Hold it, teacher!" Big Jim strode toward the front, removing his shirt, and begged, "Let me take his whippin'."[1]

Man's strongest instinct is to self-preservation; grace's highest call is to self-sacrifice.

—PAUL FROST, author

This story illustrates the truth of our Crucial Chapter, Leviticus 16. The scene is the Day of Atonement, the tenth day of the month Tishri (our mid-September to mid-October). We know it as Yom Kippur.

On this great Day of Atonement, celebrated five days before the Feast of Tabernacles, the high priest would enter the Holy of Holies to atone for his own sins and the sins of the people. This was the only day of the year the high priest could enter the presence of God inside the Holy of Holies. It was the most important day of Israel's calendar.

The word *atonement* means "to cover, to make reconciliation, to cancel." It denotes a material transaction, a compensation that results in the cancellation of sin by God. It's an "at-one-ment" with God.

Read Leviticus 16 and pay attention to the preparations required for this day.

Verses 11-14 describe the process that Aaron, the high priest, had to follow to make atonement for himself. List the main features of that procedure.

INTERESTING!
The Day of Atonement is most likely where we get our concept of *scapegoat*.

In verses 15-19, other atonements are described, all having to do with the people. But then in verses 20-22, the climax of the Day of Atonement occurs. Describe what happens in these verses.

The principle of sacrifice is that we choose to do or to suffer what apart from our love we should not choose to do or to suffer.

—WILLIAM TEMPLE, twentieth-century Anglican theologian and archbishop of York

Notice the substitutions involved in the entire event: the bull in place of Aaron, the goats in place of the people — just like Big Jim in place of little Billy.

In this, it is not difficult to see the person and work of Christ. He became not only our High Priest but also the sacrifice that the high priest offered. Look at the following comparisons.

We are not saved by theories, but by fact, and what is the fact? For whom did Christ die? Christ died for sinners. Well, then, He died for me.

—ARTHUR STANTON, nineteenth-century British preacher

LEVITICUS 16	JESUS CHRIST
High priest into the Holy of Holies	Christ into the very presence of God
High priest into the Holy of Holies with the blood of animals	Christ into the very presence of God by His own blood
High priest into the Holy of Holies once a year	Christ into the very presence of God once and for all
High priest could not make consciences perfect	Christ could cleanse consciences perfectly
This event was a mere copy	This event was the real thing
The scapegoat bore the sins away	Christ bore our sins away

Look at the last comparison once again. The sins of the people were laid on the head of the scapegoat, and it was "sent away" into the wilderness. Interestingly, the New Testament word for forgiveness means "to send away." Jesus Christ became our scapegoat and was sent away with our sins, thus providing us with forgiveness and reconciliation with God.

With this picture in mind, spend some time thanking God for what He in His unfathomable grace has done for you.

REVIEW IT!
Leviticus 16 is a Crucial Chapter describing the annual Day of Atonement, the most important day in the Jewish calendar.

MEMORY VERSE

You shall be holy, for I am holy.

LEVITICUS 11:45

LEVITICUS
[The Book of Holiness]

DAY THREE

COMPLETE READ: Chapters 12–17
QUICK READ: Chapters 2–3

INSIGHT
A person's economic
status determined the
type of sacrifice he
would bring.

NOTABLE FEATURE NUMBER 1

This week, instead of choosing a Prominent Player, we will study two Notable Features.

Imagine an Israelite worshipper who has stolen one of his neighbor's sheep. He has returned the animal to its owner but now feels the need for God's forgiveness. For an offense of this nature he must bring a *guilt offering* (Leviticus 5:14–6:7). He does so and receives God's forgiveness. But he still feels a heaviness of conscience, this time not because of the sin but because of the realization that he is a sinner at heart. Bringing a *sin offering* (4:1–5:13) relieves him of that guilt. Yet he still senses something is missing. He feels forgiven but senses a distance between himself and God. The priest counsels him to bring a *peace offering* (3:1-17), not to gain an additional sense of forgiveness but to feel a sense of restored fellowship with God. He does so and feels much better.

A few days later he is meditating on God's magnanimous pardon, forgiveness, and fellowship when his heart wells up with gratitude to God. He wants to concretely display his thanksgiving to God, so he brings a *grain offering* (2:1-16), pouring out the gratitude of his heart. Realizing how much God has done for him and how much he loves God, he longs to give himself completely to God to the best of his ability to do so. Again, he desires more than words, so he comes to the priest with a *burnt offering* (1:1-17), symbolizing a heart that says, "All that I am and have is yours, God."[2]

A habit of devout fellowship with God is the spring of all our life, and the strength of it.

—H. E. MANNING,
Catholic clergyman of the nineteenth century

The first two offerings (guilt and sin) were *compulsory*. The Israelite came as a convicted sinner. The purpose was to restore fellowship with God. The last three offerings (peace, grain, and burnt) were *voluntary*. The man came spontaneously to maintain fellowship with God. The following chart summarizes these offerings and briefly describes how each offering prefigures Jesus Christ.

OFFERING	REF.	PURPOSE	PREFIGURES CHRIST
GUILT	5:14–6:7	For sin	As atoning for damage of specific sins
SIN	4:1–5:13	For sin	As substitutionary death for sinful man
PEACE	3:1-17	For fellowship	As procuring peace with God for sinners
GRAIN	2:1-16	For thanksgiving	As offering to God a perfect life
BURNT	1:1-17	For commitment	As offering to God a totally yielded life in death

These offerings are a Notable Feature of the book of Leviticus. For the Israelite, they were the doorways of approach to God. Choose one offering and read the appropriate passage that describes it. What impressed you or impacted you as you read it?

Help my soul to breathe after holiness, after a constant devotedness to Thee, after growth in grace more abundantly every day.

—Puritan prayer in *The Valley of Vision*

The basic purpose of a sacrifice or offering is to draw near to or approach God. So in a very real sense, we can continue to give offerings to God in harmony with what our particular need is at any given moment. Thinking of sacrifice in this way helps to make sense of phrases such as "Through Him then, let us continually offer up a sacrifice of praise to God, that is, the fruit of lips that give thanks to His name" (Hebrews 13:15). What offering does this sound most like?

As you contemplate these offerings and the prefiguring of Christ that they picture, think about your needs right now. What offering do you need to bring to Him in prayer from your heart? Take time right now to do that.

Worship, then, is not a part of the Christian life; it is the Christian life.

—GERALD VANN, twentieth-century priest, teacher, and author

REVIEW IT!
A Notable Feature of the book is the description of the five offerings as different ways to approach God based on the need of the person giving the offering.

MEMORY VERSE

You shall be holy, for I am holy.

LEVITICUS 11:45

LEVITICUS
[The Book of Holiness]

DID YOU KNOW?
All adult males were
required to attend at
least three major feasts
per year.

DAY FOUR

COMPLETE READ: Chapters 18–23
QUICK READ: Chapter 23

NOTABLE FEATURE NUMBER 2

Holidays. Days throughout the year that, for whatever reason, we love and anticipate. We get a day off from work. We can sleep in. We can take advantage of a long weekend to get away or accomplish some project. We can spend time with family and friends — kicking back, relaxing, enjoying ourselves. We can revisit meaningful traditions, reenacting them year after year. And with a few of the holidays, we can concentrate on God and what He has done in the past: Christmas, Easter, even Thanksgiving.

The Israelites had their own holidays, but they were called festivals or feasts. For them, a feast was a divine appointment for collective worship. They took place at specific times and in a prescribed manner. And they were designed to periodically and regularly call the attention of the people away from their own interests and concerns and back to an awareness of their all-sufficient and glorious God. The description of these feasts is our second Notable Feature in Leviticus.

The chart that follows briefly summarizes these feasts.

*What is without periods
of rest will not endure.*

—OVID, Roman poet
(43 BC–AD 18)

Feast	Date	Ref.	Purpose	Prefigures
PASSOVER	1st month 14th day	23:5	Celebrate deliverance from Egypt	Christ our Passover Lamb
UNLEAVENED BREAD	1st month 15th–21st days	23:6-8	Pictures holiness of life	Living a holy life
FIRST FRUITS	1st month 16th day	23:9-14	Celebrate first sheaf of barley	Resurrection of Christ
PENTECOST (WEEKS)	3rd month 6th day	23:15-21	Celebrate completion of wheat harvest	Sending Holy Spirit
TRUMPETS	7th month 1st day	23:23-25	Marked beginning of New Year (civil) and coming together for Day of Atonement	Regathering of Israel
DAY OF ATONEMENT	7th month 10th day	23:26-32	Yearly sacrifice for sin by high priest	Christ our High Priest
TABERNACLES (BOOTHS)	7th month 15th–21st days	23:33-44	Celebrate end of harvest and God's faithfulness during wilderness wanderings	Israel's millennial rest

Understanding each of these feasts in depth would require hours of study. For now, read Leviticus 23:6-8, which describes the Feast of Unleavened Bread. Also read Exodus 12:15-20, which describes the same feast on the night of its inauguration. Briefly describe what you learn about its activities, purpose, and significance.

It is the Eternal Goodness calling you to return Home, to feed upon green pastures and walk beside still waters and live in the peace of the Shepherd's presence. It is the life beyond fevered strain. We are called beyond strain, to peace and power and joy and love and thorough abandonment of self.

—Thomas R. Kelly, *A Testament of Devotion*

Even a cursory overview of the Jewish feasts and festivals shows us a lot about their purpose and significance. List the reasons you think God designed this kind of yearly routine for His chosen people.

If celebrated properly, what could the typical Israelite gain from these traditional experiences?

Do you have any new thoughts regarding the celebration of our own holidays, especially those having a direct bearing on our relationship with God? If so, what?

REVIEW IT!
A second Notable Feature of the book is a description of the seven appointed feasts in chapter 23.

Memory Verse

You shall be holy, for I am holy.

LEVITICUS 11:45

LEVITICUS
[The Book of Holiness]

DAY FIVE

Chapters 24--27
QUICK READ: Chapter 26

COMPLETE READ: Chapters 24--27
QUICK READ: Chapter 26

REMEMBER
The concept of holiness
occurs eighty-seven
times in the book of
Leviticus.

A TIMELESS PRINCIPLE

In the opening chapter of his book *Rediscovering Holiness*, J. I. Packer writes,

> It is nearly sixty years since I learned at school the opening verse of a poem by Rudyard Kipling, titled "The Way Through the Woods." It goes like this:
>
> > They shut the road through the woods
> > Seventy years ago.
> > Weather and rain have undone it again
> > And now you would never know
> > There was once a road through the woods.

Packer goes on: "Again and again, when I find myself mourning the loss of a good thing . . . Kipling's verse jumps into my mind. It haunts me now as I contemplate the church's current loss of biblical truth about holiness."[3]

The situation Packer describes has not always been the case. The Puritans insisted that all of life was holiness to the Lord. John Wesley's goal in forging Methodism was to "spread scriptural holiness throughout the land."[4] And as we have seen, holiness was God's dream for His people way back in the book of Leviticus. Holiness is truly a Timeless Principle.

Read the following verses, all of which expand the "you shall be

Teach me that if I do not live a life that satisfies Thee, I shall not live a life that will satisfy myself.

—Puritan prayer in The Valley of Vision

holy" theme, and list the various components you find there: Leviticus 11:44-45; 19:2; 20:7,26.

God designed everything we have studied in the book of Leviticus to produce and promote holiness in the worship and lives of His people: the Day of Atonement with its forgiveness, the sacrifices with their varied purposes and approaches to God, and the feasts with their continual call to remember God in all of life throughout the year. God used each of these devices to create a people who would be holy, separate, unique, and set apart *from* the world and *unto* Him. His people needed every reminder and motivation God could possibly give them. And we are no different.

Later in his book, Packer gives us a poignant picture:

Lord, this is the life that no unconverted man can live, yet it is an end that every godly soul presses after. Let it be then my concern to devote myself and all to Thee.
—Puritan prayer in *The Valley of Vision*

We are all invalids in God's hospital. In moral and spiritual terms we are all sick and damaged, diseased and deformed, scarred and sore, lame and lopsided, to a far, far greater extent than we realize. Under God's care we are getting better, but we are not yet well. The modern Christian likes to dwell on present blessings rather than future prospects. Modern Christians egg each other on to testify that where once we were blind, deaf, and indeed dead so far as God was concerned, now through Christ we have been brought to life, radically transformed, and blessed with spiritual health. Thank God, there is real truth in that. But spiritual health means being holy and whole. To the extent that we fall short of being holy and whole, we are not fully healthy either.

LEVITICUS: DAY FIVE

We need to realize that the spiritual health we testify to is only partial and relative, a matter of being less sick and less incapacitated now than we were before. Measured by the absolute standard of spiritual health that we see in Jesus Christ, we are all of us no more, just as we are no less, than invalids in the process of being cured. Our spiritual life is at best a fragile convalescence, easily disrupted.[5]

What are your thoughts about Packer's statement?

DID YOU KNOW?
A burnt offering was unique in that the whole animal was consumed, signifying total dedication to God. Prior to making the sacrifice, the worshipper laid his hand on the offering, identifying himself completely with the sacrifice.

Describe holiness for a Christ-follower as you understand it.

Thy name is love, in love receive my prayer. My sins are more than the wide sea's sand, but where sin abounds, there is grace more abundant.

—Puritan prayer in *The Valley of Vision*

Write a prayer to God honestly laying before Him an appraisal of your holiness. Be sure to include a "grain offering" (gratitude) for those areas where He has produced real "healing unto holiness" in your life.

In Him the enslaved find redemption, the guilty pardon, the unholy renovation. In Him are everlasting strength for the weak, unsearchable riches for the needy, treasures of wisdom and knowledge for the ignorant, fullness for the empty.

—Puritan prayer

MEMORY VERSE

You shall be holy, for I am holy.

LEVITICUS 11:45

LEVITICUS
[The Book of Holiness]

REVIEW

1. The theme of Leviticus is you shall be _____, for I am holy.

2. Leviticus 16 is a Crucial Chapter describing the annual Day of _____, the most important day in the Jewish calendar.

3. A Notable Feature of the book is the description of the five _____ as different ways to approach God based on the need of the person giving the offering.

4. A second Notable Feature of the book is a description of the seven appointed _____ in chapter 23.

5. "You shall be _____, for I am holy."

LEVITICUS 11: _____

NUMBERS

[The Book of Unbelief]

Surely all the men who have seen My glory and My signs . . .

and have not listened to My voice, shall by no means see

the land which I swore to their fathers.

Numbers 14:22-23

FOUR

NUMBERS
[The Book of Unbelief]

INTRODUCTION

The year at Mount Sinai was over for the Israelites. God began to lead the people to the land He had promised them. They were now a well-organized nation with laws to govern behavior, priests to lead worship, a capable leader, and a mighty God who dwelt among them.

Yet when their spies reached the border of the Promised Land, they looked at the size and power of their enemies and lost the courage to enter the land. Because of their rebellion and lack of trust in God, one generation lost the privilege of entering this good land. Sadly, the people wandered in the wilderness for forty years until that entire generation died.

The book of Numbers portrays God as gracious, yet just. He longs to lead you to a good place, but you must be willing to follow, trust, and obey Him.

Numbers
[The Book of Unbelief]

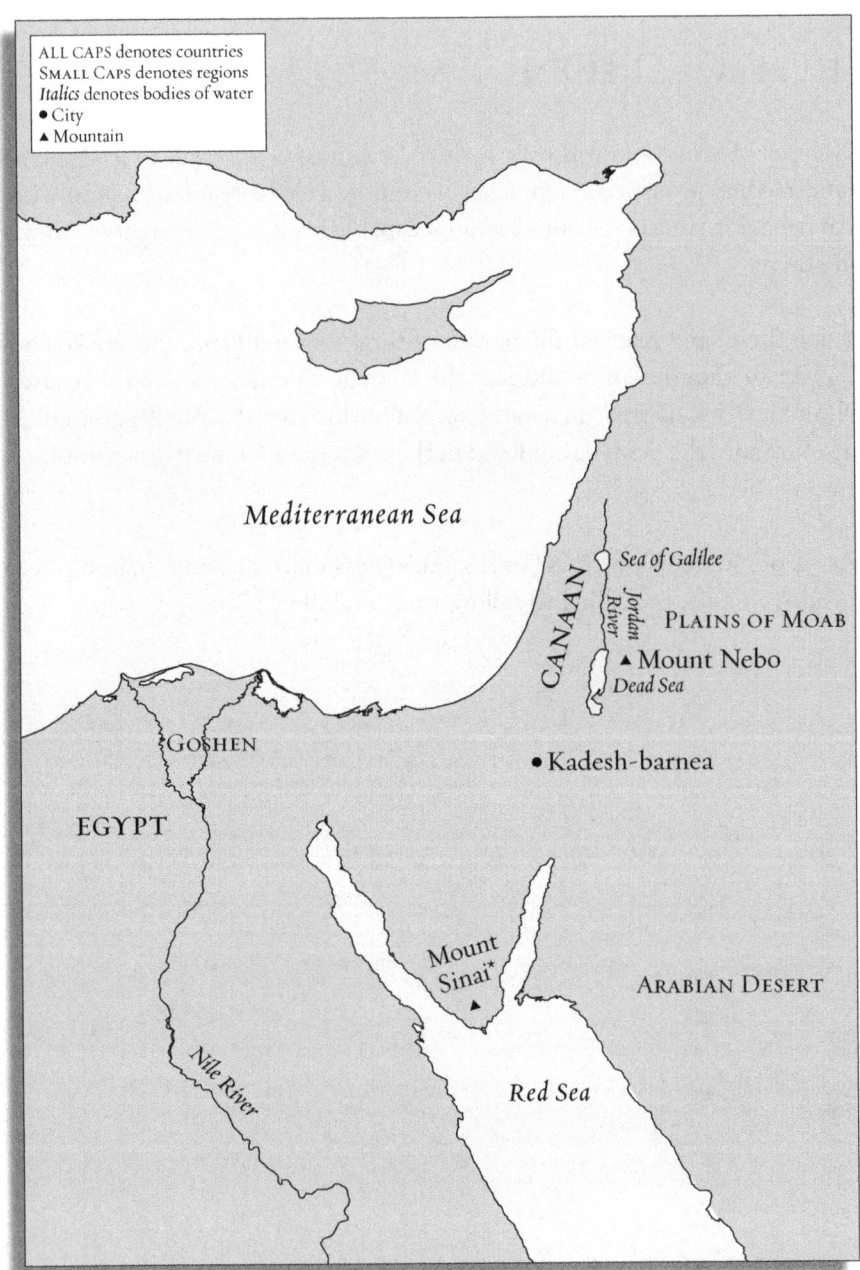

ALL CAPS denotes countries
SMALL CAPS denotes regions
Italics denotes bodies of water
● City
▲ Mountain

Mediterranean Sea

Sea of Galilee

Jordan River

CANAAN

PLAINS OF MOAB

▲ Mount Nebo

Dead Sea

GOSHEN

● Kadesh-barnea

EGYPT

Mount Sinai*

▲

ARABIAN DESERT

Nile River

Red Sea

*The actual location of Mount Sinai is believed to be here though it is still a matter of debate.

UMBERS
[The Book of Unbelief]

OVERVIEW

WHO: Author: Moses
          Main Characters: Joshua and Caleb

WHAT: Wandering in the wilderness because of unbelief

WHEN: 1444 to 1404 BC

WHERE: Mount Sinai, the wilderness, Kadesh-barnea, Plains of Moab

WHY: Because of the Israelites' unbelief and rebellion against God, He would not let an entire generation
          enter the Promised Land. They wandered in the wilderness for forty years

I. GOD _____ THE ISRAELITES TO ENTER THE PROMISED
   LAND (NUMBERS 1–10).

   A. A _____ was taken.

      1. It allowed the people to see the _____ of fighting men.

      2. _____ identified each tribe.

      3. The tribes were _____ as God commanded.

      4. _____ provided camp communication.

   B. The _____ of the Camp

      1. The priests were ordained.

      2. The tabernacle was cleansed.

      3. The diseased were removed from the camp.

   C. _____ with God

      1. The Passover was celebrated.

II. GOD _____ THE ISRAELITES FROM ENTERING THE
    PROMISED LAND (NUMBERS 11–21).

    A. They grumbled about the _____.

B. They grumbled about the _____.

C. They rebelled and refused to go into the Promised Land.

    1. God punished them by making the rebellious generation wander in the wilderness for forty years until the entire generation, except Joshua and Caleb, had all died.

    2. Yet even in the discipline, God provided for their every need.

III. GOD _____ THE NEW GENERATION OF ISRAELITES TO ENTER THE PROMISED LAND (NUMBERS 22–36).

A. Another _____ was taken and the number of fighting men had decreased.

B. They _____ the camp.

C. They reestablished _____ with God.

APPLICATION

Those who trust in God will find rest. Lack of trust brings unrest.

NUMBERS
[The Book of Unbelief]

LEARNING FOR LIFE

1. Beginning in Genesis, build the foundation for the book of Numbers (group effort).

2. Why did God instruct the people to take a census at the beginning of the book? What effect do you think it had on the people?

3. What does God's punishment of the people reveal about Him?

4. What are some ways fear prohibits you from living the abundant life God has promised in John 10:10?

5. What are some of the "giants" you face today?

NUMBERS
[The Book of Unbelief]

REMEMBER
Leviticus covered only
one month; Numbers
covers almost thirty-
nine years.

DAY ONE

COMPLETE READ: Chapters 1--8
QUICK READ: Chapter 6

THE BIG PICTURE

Reaching maturity is often a painful process, whether in the case of a young child or of a young nation. New freedoms bring new responsibilities. The book of Numbers is the story of how the Israelites, who had chafed under the imperious rule of Pharaoh, transferred their resentment of authority to Moses and ultimately to God Himself. The new limits of the divine law were sometimes as irksome as the arbitrary impositions of slavery. The responsibilities of a free people were sometimes more than Israel could fulfill. Yet in it all God was at work, molding a people for His own possession.
—DAVID KERR, *THE BIBLICAL EXPOSITOR*

*Not all those who
wander are lost.*

—J. R. R. TOLKIEN,
English professor and
author of THE LORD OF
THE RINGS trilogy

The patience of God and Moses in the book of Numbers could be a study in itself. Read its pages and you'll find endless complaining, grumbling, and faithlessness on the part of the people. In fact, one major act of faithlessness in Numbers 13 and 14 determines the character of the book and the subsequent forty years for the nation. We will study those chapters tomorrow as our Crucial Chapters.

While the name of the book comes from the two numberings of the people in chapters 1 and 26, the primary story of the book is the movement of the Israelites from Mount Sinai to the Promised Land. It should have been a quick trip, but because of that one act of faithlessness and disobedience, the Israelites spent forty years of wandering to get there! Thus, the Hebrew name for the book, which means "in the wilderness," better describes what is recorded.

As with the books of Exodus and Leviticus, Moses undoubtedly kept records of what was happening and then sometime before his death penned the book as we know it today.

The book of Leviticus provided no geographical and little chronological movement. By contrast, Numbers follows the Israelites through hundreds of miles of wandering and also through forty years. Because of the people's lack of faith, the prize of the Promised Land was taken from the old generation and given to the new—but only after the old generation had died off. The following chart summarizes the flow of the book.

INTERESTING!
A scene from Numbers is used in John 3:14 regarding Jesus Christ.

1:1 10:10	10:11 21:35	22:1 36:13
At Mount Sinai	In the Wilderness	In the Plains of Moab
Old Generation	Old Generation	New Generation
Prepared for Entering the Land	Prevented from Entering the Land	Prepared for Entering the Land
A Few Weeks	About 38 Years	A Few Months

The book of Numbers is a very human book. Frustration, disappointment, complaint, accusation, backbiting, rebellion, and faithlessness abound. But you will also find liberal doses of confession, forgiveness, respect, loyalty, faith, and submission. We can all find parts of ourselves in this story. The best news of the book? Through it all, God never ceased working to carry out His plan. And He never ceased developing His people into what He wanted them to be and what He knew they could become.

Our confidence in Christ does not make us lazy, negligent, or careless, but on the contrary it makes us active in living righteous lives and doing good. There is no self-confidence to compare with this.

—ULRICH ZWINGLI, Swiss Protestant religious reformer

As you read the book of Numbers, consider keeping a list of as many positive and negative character traits as you can find. Often, personally identifying with some of the traits lived out in the pages can be challenging and encouraging.

His words are bonds.
—WILLIAM SHAKESPEARE,
sixteenth-century English
playwright and poet

REVIEW IT!
The theme of Numbers
is wandering in the
wilderness because of
unbelief.

MEMORY VERSE

Surely all the men who have seen My glory and My signs . . . and have not listened to My voice, shall by no means see the land which I swore to their fathers.

NUMBERS 14:22-23

NUMBERS
[The Book of Unbelief]

DAY TWO

COMPLETE READ: Chapters 9–15
QUICK READ: Chapters 13–14

CRUCIAL CHAPTERS

When we look back over our lives, we often recognize periods of great importance or significance—determinative times in our journey. Maybe it was a time of testing, trial, or spiritual drought. Maybe it was a period of learning and assimilating new truth. Or perhaps it was a season when God seemed to reveal more of His kindness and blessing than ever before.

As we begin the book of Numbers, the nation of Israel has just walked through such an experience—a significant time in their nation's history. Yet as we watch their lives immediately following, we have to wonder how significant it really was to them. They had just spent a year at Mount Sinai, a year like no other in their history—a year not only decisive for Israel but for the entire human race. At no other time had God revealed so much about Himself, how He wanted to be worshipped, and how He wanted His people to live. The combination of moral, civil, and ceremonial law given to them during this time at Mount Sinai was astounding in its vastness, completeness, and loftiness. They were certainly a privileged people.

Against this background, the sin and faithlessness depicted in our Crucial Chapters (your Quick Read) stand out in stark contrast. The experiences recorded in chapters 13 and 14 take place at Kadesh-barnea just weeks following the Mount Sinai experience. And they delay entrance to the Promised Land for almost forty years.

INSIGHT
God used the forty years of wandering to turn a throng of ex-slaves into a nation ready to conquer and settle a land.

Don't doubt in the dark what God has revealed in the light.
—V. RAYMOND EDMAN, fourth president of Wheaton College

Summarize very briefly what happened at Kadesh-barnea in chapter 13. State the reports of the majority and the minority.

Describe in your own words what happened in chapter 14 regarding the following events.

Response of the people (verses 1-4):

Judgment of the people (verses 26-35):

Judgment of the majority reporters (verses 36-37):

Blessing on the minority reporters (verse 38):

Willfulness of the people (verses 40-45):

What was wrong with the thinking of those giving the majority report?

About the enemy:

About themselves:

About God:

Why do you think God's discipline was so severe?

SOBERING
Time and time again, Moses stood between Israel and utter destruction, pleading to God for mercy on their behalf (see Exodus 32:7-14; Numbers 11:1-2; 16:41-48; 21:5-9).

Faith, as Paul saw it, was a living, flaming thing leading to surrender and obedience to the commandments of Christ.

—A. W. Tozer, author and theologian of the twentieth century

God's discipline is never a pleasant experience. Can you point to a time when you sensed you were being disciplined by God? If so, when? What happened?

The New Testament helps us understand God's heart when He disciplines us. Read Hebrews 12:3-11. What encouragement does this give you?

REVIEW IT!
Chapters 13 and 14 are Crucial Chapters because they show how the unbelief of the people delayed entrance into the Promised Land for almost forty years.

MEMORY VERSE

Surely all the men who have seen My glory and My signs . . . and have not listened to My voice, shall by no means see the land which I swore to their fathers.

NUMBERS 14:22-23

NUMBERS
[The Book of Unbelief]

DAY THREE

 COMPLETE READ: Chapters 16–21
QUICK READ: Chapter 20

TWO PROMINENT PLAYERS

The story is told of a winter drought that threatened the crops in a village of Crete. The priest told his flock, "There isn't anything that will save us, except a special litany for rain. Go to your homes, fast during the week, believe, and come on Sunday for the litany of rain." The villagers heard him, fasted during the week, and went to the church on Sunday morning, but as soon as the priest saw them, he was furious. He said, "Go away; I will not do the litany. You do not believe." "But Father," they protested, "we fasted and we believe." "Believe?" he responded. "And where are your umbrellas?"[1]

In Hebrews, God tells us, "Now faith is the assurance of things hoped for, the conviction of things not seen. For by it the men of old gained approval" (Hebrews 11:1-2). Hebrews 11 goes on to list the heroes of faith:

- By faith Abel offered to God a better sacrifice than Cain.

- By faith Noah prepared an ark.

- By faith Abraham offered up Isaac.

- By faith Moses left Egypt.

- By faith the Israelites passed through the Red Sea.

So many heroes of faith.

Belief is a truth held in the mind. Faith is a fire in the heart.
—JOSEPH NEWTON, twentieth-century biographer and clergyman

FACT
Included in the census were males twenty years and older who were able to go to war.

And in the book of Numbers, we find two more and can say of them, "By faith Joshua and Caleb gave an unpopular minority report — and stood strong."

In our Crucial Chapters (13 and 14), we also find our two Prominent Players. As you know from your study yesterday, they certainly didn't carry the day with their report about the land and their recommendation of what action to take. If they had, the story in the book of Numbers would be significantly different — and much shorter. Yet even when they were defeated by the people, they were victorious before God. In the end, God turned their apparent defeat into great personal blessing — all because of their desire and determination to live out "the assurance of things hoped for, the conviction of things not seen."

Joshua and Caleb, the minority reporters, saw exactly the same thing in the Promised Land that the other ten spies saw, yet their response was so different. Read their report in Numbers 13:30 and 14:6-9 and then read the report of the other ten spies, the majority reporters, in 13:27-29 and 13:31-33. In your own words, compare and contrast the two reports.

God did not say: You will not be assailed, you will not be belabored, you will not be disquieted; but God said: You will not be overcome. God wants us to pay attention to His words, and always to be strong in our certainty, in well-being and in woe, for God loves us and delights in us.

—JULIAN OF NORWICH, religious mystic of the fourteenth century

What did Joshua and Caleb's report include that was missing from the other report?

According to Numbers 14:10-12, what were God's thoughts on the matter?

THINK ABOUT IT
Only three men of the older generation—Moses, Joshua, and Caleb—survived to the end of the book.

Read Numbers 14:22-24 and 14:36-38 and contrast the end result for the bearers of the two reports.

Hebrews 11:6 states, "Without faith it is impossible to please Him." God gives all of us "Kadesh-barnea" experiences in which He asks us to trust Him in the face of seemingly great odds and strong, contrary opinions. His desire is always to build our faith and provide opportunities for us to please Him.

Describe a time when you faced a personal "Kadesh-barnea." Was your response similar to Joshua and Caleb's or to the other ten spies?

For what is faith unless it is to believe what you do not see.

—SAINT AUGUSTINE OF HIPPO, fourth-century bishop in northern Africa

What did that experience contribute to your relationship with God?

REVIEW IT!
Joshua and Caleb are Prominent Players because they were willing to trust God in the face of great obstacles.

MEMORY VERSE

Surely all the men who have seen My glory and My signs . . . and have not listened to My voice, shall by no means see the land which I swore to their fathers.

NUMBERS 14:22-23

NUMBERS
[The Book of Unbelief]

DAY FOUR

COMPLETE READ: Chapters 22--29
QUICK READ: Chapters 22--24

A NOTABLE FEATURE

> If knowing answers to life's questions is absolutely necessary to you, then forget the journey. You will never make it, for this is a journey of unknowables — of unanswered questions, enigmas, incomprehensibles, and most of all, things unfair.
>
> —MADAME JEANNE GUYON

With our limited human perspective, it would be easy for us to label our Notable Feature "a thing unfair." Just months before Moses was to realize his dream of completing the forty-year Exodus event by leading the people across the Jordan River into the land of Canaan — the Promised Land — he was disqualified. God told Moses that because of his own sin, he would not be allowed to complete the journey. He would die before entering the land.

It is the LORD; let Him do what seems good to Him.
—ELI, the priest
(1 Samuel 3:18)

We want to shout, "Unfair!" After all he had put up with from the grumbling mass of 2.5 million people. After all the times he had pleaded with God to be merciful with the people in spite of their disrespect for and rebellion against Him. After all his faithfulness to communicate to the people what God had revealed to him, even though they were hard truths and messages to hear. After being blindsided by his own family members who rebelled against his leadership. After all that — now this? Unfair! But those are human thoughts and feelings. And God has told us that "My thoughts are not your thoughts, Nor are your ways My ways" (Isaiah 55:8).

Read the story in Numbers 20:1-13 and describe the situation.

If you were Moses or Aaron, what would you be feeling and thinking after hearing the people's complaints in verses 2-5?

What do you think Moses expected when he went to the doorway of the tent of meeting and fell on his face (verse 6)?

Describe as many components of Moses' misconduct as you see in verses 9-11.

Faith is deliberate confidence in the character of God whose ways you may not understand at the time.

—OSWALD CHAMBERS, author of *My Utmost for His Highest*

In verse 12, God gave Moses the reason for his disqualification. What do you think God meant by that reason?

In Numbers 27:12-23 God again initiated a discussion with Moses about his disqualification from leading the people into the Promised Land. What does Moses' reaction to God say about him?

Based on these two passages (Numbers 20:1-13; 27:12-23), what thoughts do you have about:

Moses

God

Yourself

Pray whatever is appropriate for yourself at this moment.

MEMORY VERSE

Surely all the men who have seen My glory and My signs . . . and have not listened to My voice, shall by no means see the land which I swore to their fathers.

NUMBERS 14:22-23

NUMBERS
[The Book of Unbelief]

INTERESTING!
In God's arrangement
of the twelve tribes in
the camp of Israel, He
placed the nearest
relatives closest to one
another. The tribes
were descended from
four different mothers,
all wives of Jacob.

DAY FIVE

 COMPLETE READ: Chapters 30--36
QUICK READ: Chapter 9:15-23

A TIMELESS PRINCIPLE

At one time or another all of us ask, "What does God want me to do? What is the will of God for me in this situation?" And most of the time, if we could just figure it out, we wouldn't fight it! We simply want to know it. Have you ever wanted to know God's will so badly that you wished for a secret formula or unmistakable sign?

This certainly is not *just* a modern challenge. For thousands of years, people have concocted methods of finding the will of God or of the gods. In the Ancient Near East during the time of the Pentateuch, divination was a favorite method, performed in several ways. Seekers would pour clear water into a goblet, drop pieces of gold, silver, or precious stones into it, and observe and interpret their movements. Another option was to pour water into a goblet, set it in the sun, and read the motions of the sun playing on the water. A third way would be to pour water into oil, oil into water, or wine into any other liquid and watch the liquids interact to determine the mind of the gods.

Even the book of Proverbs discusses a method: "The lot is cast into the lap, but its every decision is from the LORD" (16:33). Also, the priests of the Old Testament carried the Urim and Thummim, most likely two nearly identical stones, in a pouch on their breastplate. They could determine the will of God by drawing one out of the pouch (see Exodus 28:30). And then there was Gideon's fleece (see Judges 6:36-40). The need to

Where you have absolute solutions, however, you have no need of faith.

—FLANNERY O'CONNOR,
twentieth-century
American writer

discover God's will is certainly a Timeless Principle *and* a timeless challenge.

We see in today's Quick Read that God gave the Israelites a way to know His will for their movements during these wilderness wanderings. Look at the passage again and briefly describe the procedure as God designed it.

When we read this passage, many of us find ourselves wishing that determining God's will could be that easy and clear-cut for us. Who could miss a cloud or misinterpret when it moves or stops? What are the advantages of God's will being that clear?

What are the disadvantages of it being that clear?

We don't get a mobile cloud over our experiences, leading us step by step. Determining God's will can be a challenge. What frustrations do you experience in this area?

In His will is our peace.
—Dante Alighieri, Italian national epic poet of the fourteenth century

What basic components are involved when you seek to know God's will?

How do you feel about your understanding and practice of this delicate spiritual activity?

If you need to grow in this area, seek someone you trust to talk with.

Just a reminder: It's easy to get so caught up in finding God's will for which house to buy, what job to take, what gift to buy, and so on that we get careless about His very clear and undebatable moral will. In reality, we make more daily decisions regarding His moral will than any other. And many times, proper choices in that regard make other decisions clearer. Plus, we have a guide the Israelites did not have — the Holy Spirit.

MEMORY VERSE

Surely all the men who have seen My glory and My signs . . . and have not listened to My voice, shall by no means see the land which I swore to their fathers.

NUMBERS 14:22-23

UMBERS
[The Book of Unbelief]

REVIEW

1. The theme of Numbers is wandering in the wilderness because of

   _____.

2. Chapters 13 and 14 are Crucial Chapters because they show how the unbelief of the people delayed entrance into the _____ Land for almost forty years.

3. _____ and _____ are Prominent Players because they were willing to trust God in the face of great obstacles.

4. Our Notable Feature is Moses' _____ from entering the Promised Land, proving once again that God's ways are not our ways.

5. "Surely all the men who have seen My _____ and My signs . . . and have not listened to My voice, shall by no means see the land which I swore to their fathers."

   NUMBERS 14: _____-_____

DEUTERONOMY

[The Book of Obedience]

*I have set before you life and death, the blessing and
the curse. So choose life in order that you may live.*

DEUTERONOMY 30:19

FIVE

DEUTERONOMY
[The Book of Obedience]

INTRODUCTION

Deuteronomy begins with the Israelites at yet another crossroad: the border of Canaan, the Promised Land. Moses understood that because of his disobedience, he would not be allowed to enter the Promised Land with them. As he looked over the Jordan River, he could see the land that they would inhabit, a land flowing with milk and honey. Soon he would die, but he used the time he had left to further instruct the people and remind them that God was in the past, the present, and the future. Deuteronomy records his three messages to the new generation.

In the first one, Moses reviewed what God had done for the people. The second teaching told the Israelites what God expected of them. And the last sermon painted a picture of what God would do for them. Like Leviticus, Deuteronomy is an instructional book. We learn that obedience brings blessings, while disobedience brings curses or God's punishment.

God's patience, faithfulness, and great love are clear in Deuteronomy. The book is also a reminder of God's seriousness about obedience. You will learn how obedience is the key to experiencing the greatest amount of joy and peace in your life and how it can impact future generations for great good.

Deuteronomy

[The Book of Obedience]

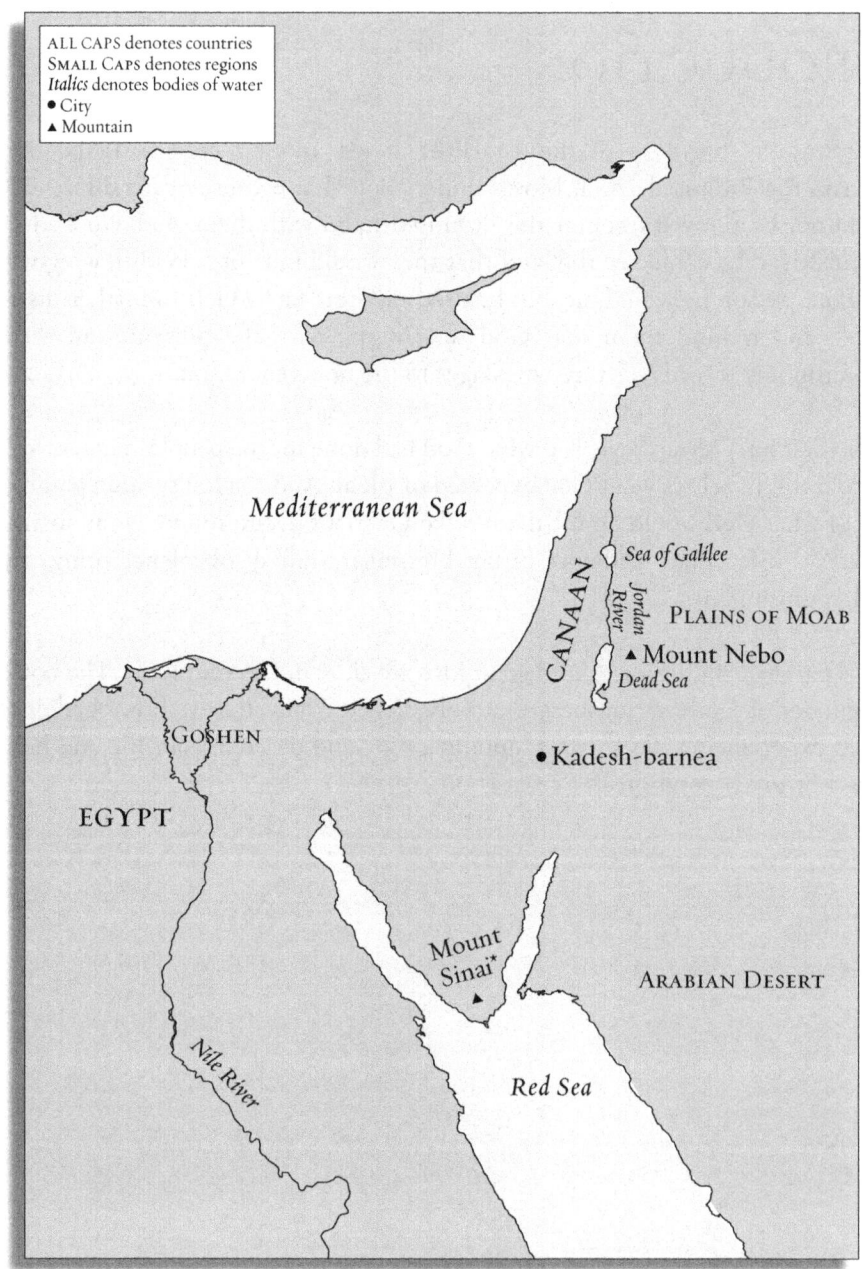

ALL CAPS denotes countries
SMALL CAPS denotes regions
Italics denotes bodies of water
● City
▲ Mountain

Mediterranean Sea

CANAAN

Sea of Galilee

Jordan River

PLAINS OF MOAB

▲ Mount Nebo

Dead Sea

GOSHEN

● Kadesh-barnea

EGYPT

Mount Sinai*

ARABIAN DESERT

▲

Nile River

Red Sea

*The actual location of Mount Sinai is believed to be here though it is still a matter of debate.

DEUTERONOMY
[The Book of Obedience]

OVERVIEW

WHO: Author: Moses

WHAT: Preparing the new generation to enter the land

WHEN: 1405 BC. The book covers a period of about one month

WHERE: The people were camped east of the Jordan River in view of the Promised Land

WHY: Moses prepared the new generation to enter the Promised Land

I. HISTORICAL: REMEMBRANCES OF THE PAST (DEUTERONOMY 1–11)

    A. Moses reminded them of man's past _____ (Deuteronomy 1).

    B. Moses reminded them of God's past _____ (Deuteronomy 2–11).

II. LEGAL: INSTRUCTIONS FOR THE FUTURE (DEUTERONOMY 12–30)

    A. There are two reasons to obey God's laws:

        1. Your _____ will go better.

        2. It shows our _____ for God.

    B. God's laws the people needed to obey in the land were:

        1. _____ laws or statutes

        2. _____ laws or judgments

        3. _____ laws or testimonies

III. Personal: Present Choices Impact the Future
(Deuteronomy 31–34)

   A. Moses' _____ kept him from entering the
      Promised Land.

   B. Moses looked into the land and _____.

Application

   Our obedience or disobedience affects future generations.

Deuteronomy
[The Book of Obedience]

Learning for Life

1. Beginning in Genesis, build the foundation for the book of Deuteronomy (group effort).

2. Describe the Pentateuch.

   a. Who wrote it? What are the main messages from each book?

   b. Make one application to your own life from each book.

3. Why do you think it was so important for Moses to remind the people of their past and the past of their fathers?

4. What three "sermons" would you give the younger generation if you knew they would listen and take heed?

DEUTERONOMY
[The Book of Obedience]

DAY ONE

 COMPLETE READ: Chapters 1--8
QUICK READ: Chapter 6

THE BIG PICTURE

You leave your hometown and move to a new city. Your first child is born. Your last child leaves home. Times of transition can be exciting—and challenging. The past must be put away, yet always honored and remembered. The future, not yet arrived, must be anticipated and prepared for.

The book of Deuteronomy marks a significant time of transition for the nation of Israel:

- From the old generation to the new generation

- From the wilderness wanderings to the Canaan settlement

- From life in tents to life in houses

- From manna and quail to a feast of milk, honey, corn, and wine

- From the leadership of Moses to the leadership of Joshua

- From anticipating the Promised Land to experiencing the Promised Land

And in order to remember the past and prepare for the future, God gave Moses a unique time with this new generation just before they entered Canaan to conquer and settle the land. They stopped just east of the Jordan River where they could look

There is nothing permanent except change.

—HERACLITUS, ancient Greek philosopher

across and see their promised inheritance. It is at this place that Moses chose to instruct them one last time. He challenged the people through a number of long sermons. Then he ascended Mount Nebo, looked long over the Promised Land, died, and was buried by God.

As with the rest of the Pentateuch, Deuteronomy was authored by Moses — except, of course, the recording of his death. Most likely Joshua, the nation's new leader, composed that narrative. The chart that follows gives an overview of the content of Deuteronomy.

CHAPTERS 1–11	CHAPTERS 12–30	CHAPTERS 31–34
Remembrances of the Past	Instructions for the Future	Present Choices Impact the Future
Historical	Legal	Personal
Key: 8:2	Key: 29:10-13	Key: 34:1-12

Time: 1–2 Months   **Place:** In the Plains of Moab

The Hebrew title for Deuteronomy means "the words," taken from the opening phrase in 1:1. The English title follows the title of the Greek translation of the Old Testament and means "second law." Both titles are properly descriptive. Deuteronomy is "the words" of Moses and it is a "second law" — not new, but restated. Deuteronomy is not a new covenant, but a covenant renewal. Moses reviewed and restated for the new generation much of the revelation God gave the old generation at Mount Sinai.

Because of their disobedience at Kadesh-barnea, the old generation had died — only Moses, Joshua, and Caleb remained — and it was the children of that old generation that comprised the nation at that time. Thus, last minute instruction and challenge to obedience by their leader was crucial. Preparing the new generation to enter the land is the theme of Deuteronomy.

DID YOU KNOW? Deuteronomy has been called "Moses' Upper Desert Discourse."

The art of progress is to preserve order amid change, and to preserve change amid order.
—ALFRED NORTH WHITEHEAD, English logician, mathematician, and philosopher

Spend a few moments meditating on the memory verse below. What most impresses you about its message?

REVIEW IT!
The theme of Deuteronomy is preparing the new generation to enter the land.

MEMORY VERSE

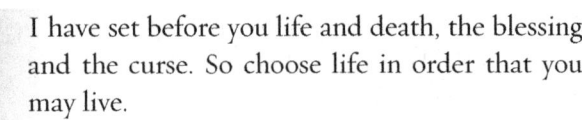

I have set before you life and death, the blessing and the curse. So choose life in order that you may live.

DEUTERONOMY 30:19

DEUTERONOMY

[The Book of Obedience]

DAY TWO

COMPLETE READ: Chapters 9--15
QUICK READ: Chapter 11

A CRUCIAL CHAPTER

About AD 30, a young Jewish teacher was confronted by the leading religious scholars of his day in regard to a number of practical and theological issues. The Pharisees thought they could stump the young teacher by asking the question, "Teacher, which is the great commandment in the Law?" He unhesitatingly answered them, "'YOU SHALL LOVE THE LORD YOUR GOD WITH ALL YOUR HEART, AND WITH ALL YOUR SOUL, AND WITH ALL YOUR MIND.' This is the great and foremost commandment" (Matthew 22:36-38). The young teacher was Jesus, the Son of God. And His answer was a direct quote from the Old Testament book of Deuteronomy, from the very chapter we will study today as our Crucial Chapter—chapter 6. At the end of our study, we will focus on that quote.

In Deuteronomy 1–5, Moses reviewed some of the Israelites' history, instructing the new generation to obey God's laws. He restated the moral law, the Ten Commandments, given to the people by God at Mount Sinai about thirty-eight years earlier. In Deuteronomy 6, his heart was heavy with the message and exhortation he had to give to the people. He pleaded passionately with them—"Hear, O Israel!"—to take his words deep into their hearts. He knew if they did not, their hearts would be lost.

To be truly Christian means to see Christ everywhere, to know Him as all in all.
—MADELEINE L'ENGLE,
American writer
and poet

In 6:1-3 and 6:16-19, how did he exhort them, and what did he say the benefits would be if they followed his exhortation?

When God brought them into the land, they would benefit from things they had nothing to do with providing. In 6:10-15, how did Moses describe this and what did he indicate may be their biggest problem to face?

The Israelites' relationship with God was always a family affair. The phrases "our fathers," "our sons," and "our grandsons" occur with amazing regularity throughout the Old Testament. And this chapter is no exception, particularly regarding "sons." Verse 2 has already introduced the idea: "So that you and your son and your grandson might fear the LORD your God."

Read 6:6-9 and 6:20-25. Write down as many thoughts as you can from these verses about Moses' and God's desire for each generation to pass on to the next generation a vital relationship with their God. Looking through these verses for principles and actions may be helpful.

Principles:

Actions:

DID YOU KNOW?
Wilderness simply means "uninhabited land."

Jesus' answer to the Pharisees' question, "Which is the greatest commandment in the Law?" is tucked away near the beginning of Deuteronomy 6. Most likely, Moses intended it to be the motivation for everything they were instructed and encouraged to do, not only in this chapter, but in the entire book of Deuteronomy.

Read verses 4 and 5. Describe in your own words what verse 5 means and what motivation it provides to live out everything else in this chapter.

When spirituality is viewed as a journey, the way to spiritual wholeness is seen to lie in an increasingly faithful response to the One whose purpose shapes our path, whose grace redeems our detours and whose transforming presence meets us at each turn in the road.

—M. ROBERT MULHOLLAND, author of *Invitation to a Journey*

Where does this kind of love for God rank in your various motivations for serving God?

Are you content with its place? If not, how could you seek growth in this area?

MEMORY VERSE

I have set before you life and death, the blessing and the curse. So choose life in order that you may live.

DEUTERONOMY 30:19

DEUTERONOMY

[The Book of Obedience]

DAY THREE

Complete Read: Chapters 16–22
Quick Read: Chapters 17–18

A Prominent Player

In the last speech he ever gave, Martin Luther King Jr. gave a stirring appeal to look to the future and to expect things to be different than they were at the present time. And in that speech, he clearly alluded to the last chapter of the book of Deuteronomy and our Prominent Player, Moses. King said,

> I've been to the mountaintop. . . . Like anybody, I would like to live a long life. Longevity has its place. But I'm not concerned about that now. I just want to do God's will. And He's allowed me to go up to the mountain. And I've looked over. And I've seen the promised land. I may not get there with you. But I want you to know tonight, that we, as a people, will get to the promised land. And I'm happy, tonight. . . . Mine eyes have seen the glory of the coming of the Lord.[1]

Following that speech, King returned to his motel room, was struck by an assassin's bullet, and died. He was right. He never reached the Promised Land he had dreamed of and struggled so to reach.

For Moses, the scene was similar. He literally went to the top of a mountain, looked over the actual Promised Land, and then died. He saw but never entered the Promised Land he had dreamed of and struggled so to reach.

JUST A THOUGHT
Booker T. Washington said, "Success should be measured not so much by the position one has reached in life as by the obstacles which one has overcome while trying to succeed." How true of Moses.

Moses went up on Mount Cyanide to get the ten commandments; he died before he ever reached Canada.

—A child from *A Speaker's Sourcebook* by Virgil Hurley

On Day Four of Numbers, we studied the event that disqualified Moses from entering the land. Moses restates that scene again in this book.

Read Deuteronomy 32:48-52 to refresh your memory. Do you have any new thoughts about this episode as it is restated here?

AMAZING!
It was an eighteen to twenty day trip from Mount Sinai to the Promised Land. It took the Israelites forty years.

Read Deuteronomy 34:1-3. What do you think Moses was thinking and feeling in his last moments?

The stewardship of intimacy with the Almighty carries with it a heightened sense of accountability.

—REGGIE MCNEAL, author of *A Work of Heart*

God's statement in verse 4 of chapter 34 is so significant. God was about to fulfill His promise to Abraham — a promise He had made seven hundred years earlier! Moses would not enter the land, but God told him that seven hundred years of waiting was nearly over. Moses' love for the people he had led — despite their grumbling and rebellion — never dimmed. We can only imagine the joy he felt for the people, knowing they would finally enter the Promised Land.

Verses 5-12 describe Moses' death, his burial by God, and God's commendations of him. Thoughtfully read these verses (as well as Numbers 12:3). Write down everything you see of God's appraisal of Moses.

Thinking back on your knowledge of Moses' life — his relationship with God, his huge responsibility of leading 2.5 million people, his love for them even in their times of grumbling and rebellion, his struggles, his own disappointment of never reaching the Promised Land, and God's appraisal of him in Deuteronomy 34 — what do you see in our Prominent Player that you would like to imitate?

Pray, asking God to enable you to make your desires a reality.

MEMORY VERSE

I have set before you life and death, the blessing and the curse. So choose life in order that you may live.

DEUTERONOMY 30:19

DEUTERONOMY
[The Book of Obedience]

NOTE
Deuteronomy refers
back to the first four
books of the
Pentateuch 259 times.

DAY FOUR

COMPLETE READ: Chapters 23--30
QUICK READ: Chapter 28

A NOTABLE FEATURE

As J. I. Packer discusses the idea of studying about and knowing God in the first chapter of his classic book *Knowing God,* he writes,

> Knowing about God is crucially important for the living of our lives. As it would be cruel to an Amazonian tribesman to fly him to London, put him down without explanation in Trafalgar Square and leave him, as one who knew nothing of English or England, to fend for himself, so we are cruel to ourselves if we try to live in this world without knowing about the God whose world it is and who runs it. The world becomes a strange, mad, painful place, and life in it a disappointing and unpleasant business, for those who do not know about God. Disregard the study of God, and you sentence yourself to stumble and blunder through life blindfolded, as it were, with no sense of direction and no understanding of what surrounds you.[2]

It is the heart that is not yet sure of its God that is afraid to laugh in His presence.

—GEORGE MACDONALD, Scottish novelist and poet of the nineteenth century

In a similar vein, A. W. Tozer makes this statement in his book *The Knowledge of the Holy*: "Were we able to extract from any man a complete answer to the question, 'What comes into your mind when you think about God?' we might predict with certainty the spiritual future of that man."[3]

If these two men are correct, then our primary pursuit in life should be knowing God through study and personal relationship.

Interestingly, Moses indicated a similar passion. Though we can learn of God through every book in the Bible, Deuteronomy seems to have more explicit teaching about and illustrations of who God is than almost any other book. This makes sense because Moses was exhorting a new generation to the highest possible calling: knowing, loving, and obeying their God. Thus, a Notable Feature of the book of Deuteronomy is its glimpses and portraits of who God really is. As you prepare to investigate these passages, ask God to give you new and true insights into Him.

Read the following groups of verses, state what they as a group teach about God, and try to illustrate from your life how you have experienced that particular truth of God.

Deuteronomy 6:10; 7:9; 9:5; 10:11; 29:13

A truth about God and how it is shown:

An illustration from your life:

Deuteronomy 3:24; 4:34; 6:21-23; 7:17-21; 9:29

A truth about God and how it is shown:

INSIGHT
A clear picture of Jesus Christ as a prophet is given in Deuteronomy 18:15.

Knowing God. Is there any greater theme? Is there any nobler goal? Is there any greater good? Is there any deeper longing in the human heart? . . . For this we were made, and for this we were redeemed.

—J. I. PACKER, theologian, professor, and author of *Knowing God*

DID YOU KNOW?
After Moses' death, the next time we see him is in Mark 9:2-4, talking to Jesus on a mountain.

An illustration from your life:

Deuteronomy 4:37; 7:7-8,12-13; 10:14-15

A truth about God and how it is shown:

An illustration from your life:

Deuteronomy 4:24; 5:9; 6:15

A truth about God and how it is shown:

Be Thou my vision,
    O Lord of my heart;
Nought be all else to
    me, save that Thou
    art—
Thou my best thought,
    by day or by night,
Waking or sleeping,
    Thy presence my
    light.
—*Be Thou My Vision,*
ancient Irish hymn

An illustration from your life:

Deuteronomy 1:34-38; 3:26-27; 9:22

A truth about God and how it is shown:

An illustration from your life:

Reinforce my conviction, Father, that nothing can separate me from your love, that there are no places where you are absent, no times when you are asleep, that you are in all times and all places for me in Jesus Christ. Amen.

—EUGENE PETERSON, pastor and translator of *The Message*

Certainly there are many other portrayals of the person of God in this book, but from the few you have discovered, what has impressed you the most? Turn these thoughts of God into a prayer, either spoken or written.

MEMORY VERSE

I have set before you life and death, the blessing and the curse. So choose life in order that you may live.

DEUTERONOMY 30:19

REVIEW IT!
A Notable Feature in the book of Deuteronomy is the array of pictures of the person of God.

DEUTERONOMY
[The Book of Obedience]

DAY FIVE

COMPLETE READ: Chapters 31–34
QUICK READ: Chapter 31

A TIMELESS PRINCIPLE

There are three things I always forget. Names, faces and — the third I can't remember.

—ITALO SVERO, ITALIAN NOVELIST

I've a grand memory for forgetting, David.

—ROBERT LOUIS STEVENSON, *KIDNAPPED*

O Lord! Thou knowest how busy I must be this day; if I forget Thee, do not then forget me.

—SIR JACOB ASTLEY, PRAYER BEFORE
THE BATTLE OF EGDEHILL, 1642

But men are men; the best sometimes forget.

—WILLIAM SHAKESPEARE, *Othello*

To forget is human. So often the consequences of forgetfulness are inconsequential. But sometimes, our forgetfulness costs us dearly.

In the book of Deuteronomy, Moses passionately addresses our penchant for forgetting — especially as it relates to God. Moses knew spiritual amnesia was deadly. Throughout the book, the word *forget* and its forms occur thirteen times, and the word *remember* occurs fourteen times. This theme is so strong in Deuteronomy that it has been called the "Book of Remembrance."

Jesus understood how easy it is for us to forget. During His last meal with the disciples before His death, He instituted what we call Communion, the Lord's Supper, or the Eucharist by saying,

"This is My body which is given for you; do this in *remembrance* of Me" (Luke 22:19, emphasis added). A remembrance. A ritual. A way to regularly recall to our minds the greatest sacrifice ever made. It helps us to not forget.

As you read the following verses, jot down your thoughts to the questions below: Deuteronomy 4:9-10,23; 6:10-12; 7:17-19; 8:2,11-14,19; 9:7; 24:18.

What does Moses warn them not to forget?

What are some of the causes of their forgetting?

What are some of the results of their forgetting?

REMEMBER
To the readers of his second letter, Peter said he would not hesitate "to stir you up by way of reminder" (2 Peter 1:13; 3:1).

Unless we remember we cannot understand.
—E. M. FORSTER, twentieth-century British novelist

Having thought through the Israelites' penchant for forgetfulness, what do you see that is also true of you at times?

What spiritual habits, practices, disciplines, or reminders can you build into your life to safeguard against the fact that "to forget is human"?

This I recall to my mind, therefore I have hope. The L ORD's lovingkindnesses indeed never cease, for His compassions never fail.

—The prophet Jeremiah (Lamentations 3:21-22)

MEMORY VERSE

 I have set before you life and death, the blessing and the curse. So choose life in order that you may live.

DEUTERONOMY 30:19

DEUTERONOMY
[The Book of Obedience]

REVIEW

1. The theme of Deuteronomy is _____ the new generation to enter the land.

2. Chapter 6 is a Crucial Chapter because it is Moses' passionate _____ to love God with all our heart, soul, and might.

3. _____ is the Prominent Player in Deuteronomy based on God's appraisal of him in chapter 34.

4. A Notable Feature in the book of Deuteronomy is the array of _____ of the person of God.

5. "I have set before you life and death, the _____ and the curse. So choose life in order that you may live."

DEUTERONOMY 30: _____

COMPREHENSIVE REVIEW OF
THE PENTATEUCH

GENESIS

1. The theme of Genesis is the book of _____.

2. Chapter 3 is a Crucial Chapter in its description of man's first sin and God's first promise of _____.

3. _____ is a Prominent Player because God chose him to be the father of the nation that would bring blessing to all the families of the world.

4. The Notable Feature of the book is God's _____ in choosing Egypt as the place to develop His nation.

5. "I will establish My _____ between Me and you and your descendants after you."

GENESIS 17: _____

EXODUS

1. The theme of Exodus is you shall have no other _____ before Me.

2. Chapters 11 and 12 are Crucial Chapters because they show us how the _____ is a defining moment in God's plan to bring salvation to Israel and the world.

3. _____ is the Prominent Player in Exodus as God works with him to help him become what he needs to be.

4. The _____ is a Notable Feature of Exodus because it represents the presence of God and our way of approach to God.

5. "I am the LORD your God, who brought you out of the land of Egypt, out of the house of _____."

EXODUS 20: _____

LEVITICUS

1. The theme of Leviticus is you shall be _____, for I am holy.

2. Leviticus 16 is a Crucial Chapter describing the annual Day of _____, the most important day in the Jewish calendar.

3. A Notable Feature of the book is the description of the five _____ as different ways to approach God based on the need of the person giving the offering.

4. A second Notable Feature of the book is a description of the seven appointed _____ in chapter 23.

5. "You shall be _____, for I am holy."

LEVITICUS 11: _____

NUMBERS

1. The theme of Numbers is wandering in the wilderness because of _____.

2. Chapters 13 and 14 are Crucial Chapters because they show how the unbelief of the people delayed entrance into the _____ Land for almost forty years.

3. _____ and _____ are Prominent Players because they were willing to trust God in the face of great obstacles.

4. Our Notable Feature is Moses' _____ from entering the Promised Land, proving once again that God's ways are not our ways.

5. "Surely all the men who have seen My _____ and My signs . . . and have not listened to My voice, shall by no means see the land which I swore to their fathers."

NUMBERS 14: _____-_____

DEUTERONOMY

1. The theme of Deuteronomy is _____ the new generation to enter the land.

2. Chapter 6 is a Crucial Chapter because it is Moses' passionate _____ to love God with all our heart, soul, and might.

3. _____ is the Prominent Player in Deuteronomy based on God's appraisal of him in chapter 34.

4. A Notable Feature in the book of Deuteronomy is the array of _____ of the person of God.

5. "I have set before you life and death, the _____ and the curse. So choose life in order that you may live."

DEUTERONOMY 30: _____

CONGRATULATIONS!

You've just completed the journey through The Pentateuch. It has been quite an adventure! In these first five books of the Bible, you have traveled from the beauty and perfection of the Garden of Eden through a worldwide flood, idolatry in Canaan, slavery in Egypt, and wandering in the wilderness to the border of the Promised Land. You have witnessed miracles of mind-boggling proportions: horrific plagues, the parting of the Red Sea, rocks that brought forth water, food that dropped from heaven, and a donkey that talked. But above all else, you have stood in the presence of God Almighty and have seen His character: His power in Genesis, His faithfulness in Exodus, His wisdom in Leviticus, His justice in Numbers, and His love in Deuteronomy.

And now the adventure continues! Every page of this Amazing Collection has been painted with the love of God for His children. As you leave The Pentateuch and move into The Kingdom Books (Joshua through 2 Kings), you will walk with men and women who are courageous and who are weak, some who are good and some who are evil. You will meet the faithful and the faithless. And you will learn more about the character of God: His power, goodness, patience, and lovingkindness.

You will also hear real-life stories from people who testify to God's power in their lives today, and you will have opportunities to worship — through music — the Almighty God of the Bible. The adventure continues!

CHRONOLOGICAL RELATIONSHIP OF THE OLD TESTAMENT BOOKS

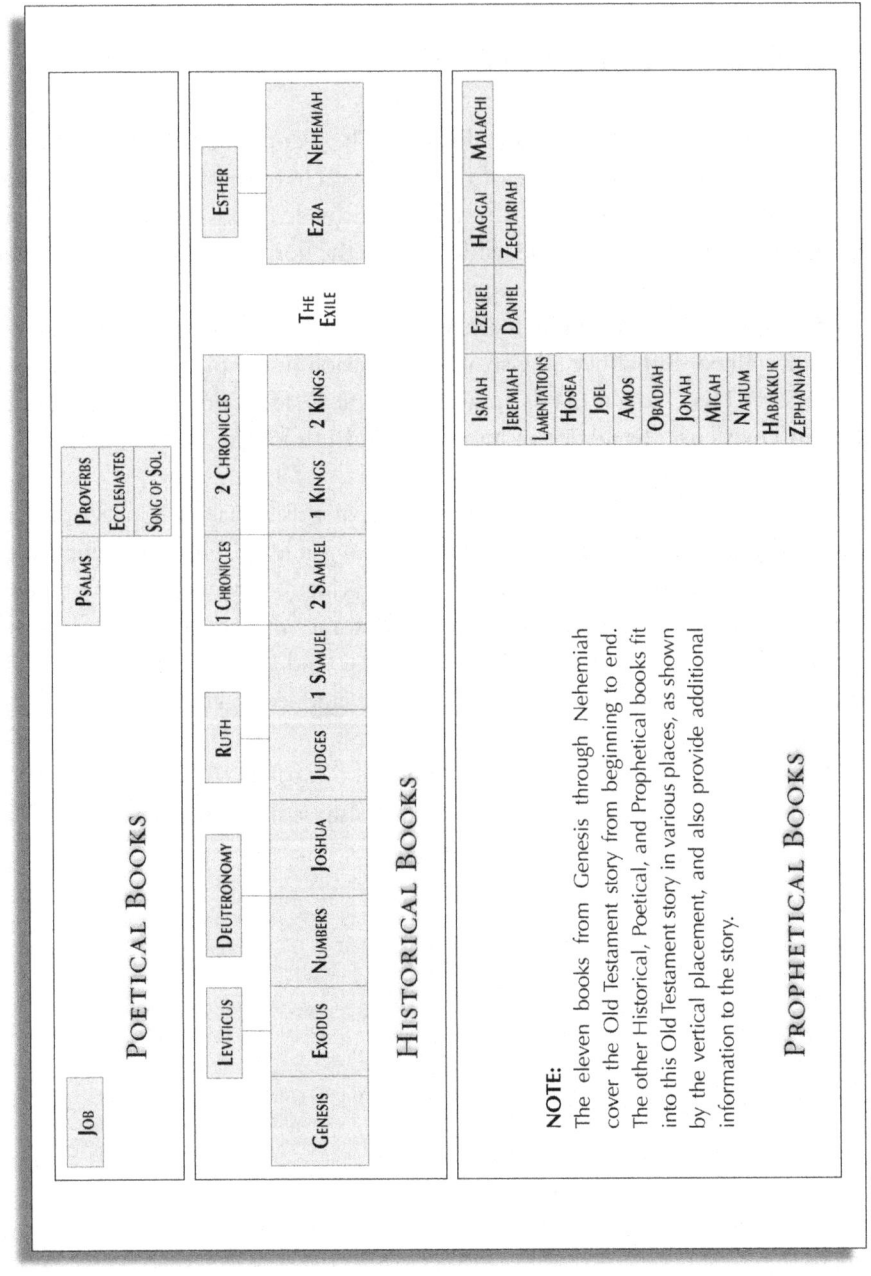

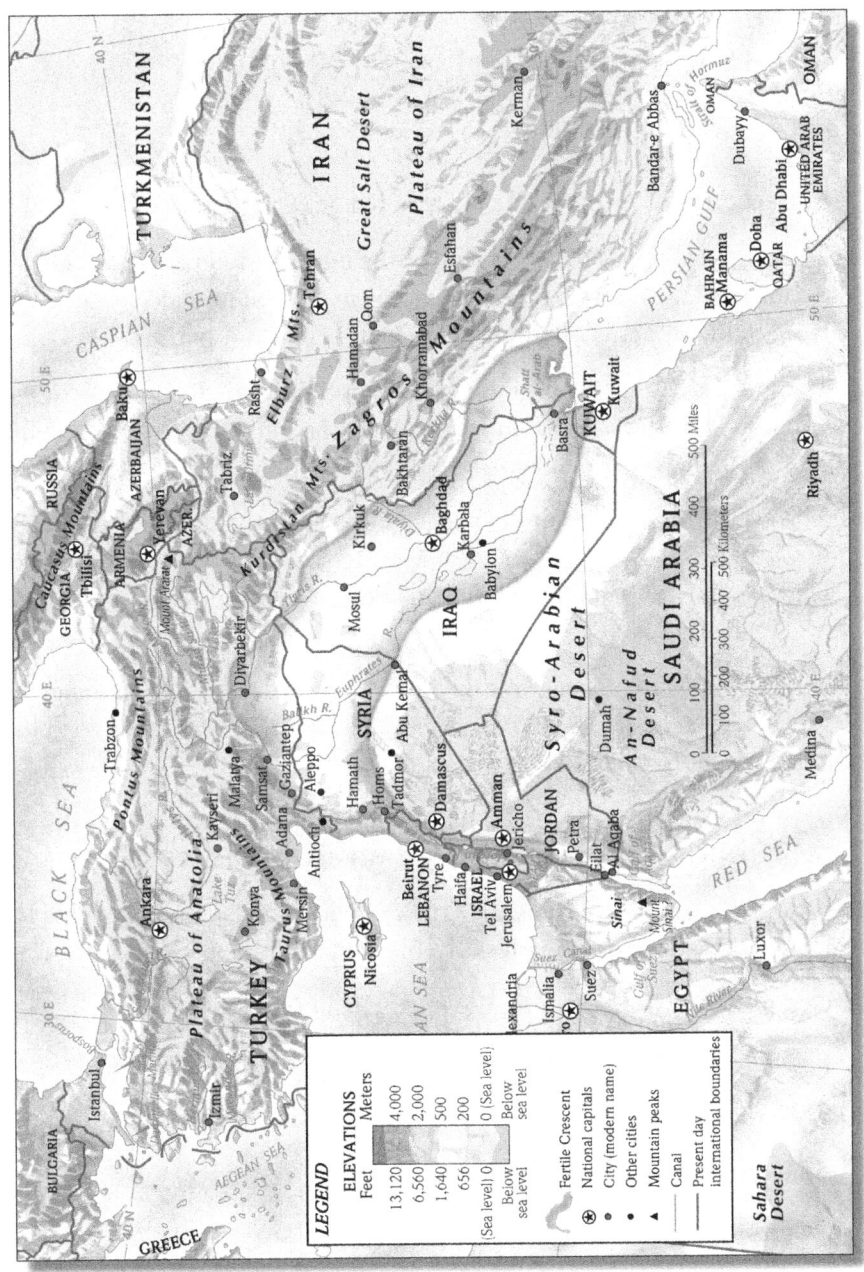

Modern States and the Ancient Near East from Holman Bible Atlas © 1998. Holman Bible Publishers. Used by permission.

ANSWER KEY TO OUTLINES

GENESIS

   I. THE BEGINNING OF THE HUMAN RACE (GENESIS 1–11)

     A. The <u>CREATION</u> was the beginning of the universe and people (Genesis 1–2). Adam and Eve were the first man and woman. God provided a garden for them to live in perfect harmony with nature, one another, and Him.

     B. The <u>FALL</u> (sin) was the beginning of separation from God and physical death (Genesis 3). Eve was tempted by Satan, ate the only fruit that was off-limits, invited Adam to share in her sin, and together they rebelled against God.

     C. The <u>FLOOD</u> was the result of violence in the land that brought the judgment of God (Genesis 6–10). Noah was a righteous man who found favor with God. God instructed him to build an ark, and when the flood came, Noah and his family were saved.

     D. The beginning of languages at the Tower of Babel was the beginning of <u>NATIONS</u> (Genesis 11). God confused their language when they tried to build a monument to their own greatness.

   II. THE BEGINNING OF THE CHOSEN RACE (GENESIS 12–50)

God chose one man to become the father of a nation (Israel) that would love and worship God and be an example and a blessing to all the nations of the world.

     A. God made a <u>COVENANT</u> promise to Abraham (Genesis 12).

       1. Abraham's family would become a great <u>NATION</u>.

       2. All the families of the earth would be blessed by his <u>DESCENDANTS</u>.

       3. His descendants would be given <u>LAND</u>.

     B. God's Chosen People: The Patriarchs of Israel (Genesis 21–26).

1. The son of Abraham was ISAAC (Genesis 21–26).

2. The two sons of Isaac were JACOB and Esau (Genesis 27–36). Jacob was the son chosen by God to carry on the blessings of the covenant.

3. Jacob had TWELVE sons who became the twelve tribes of Israel (Genesis 30–35).

4. Jacob's favorite son was JOSEPH (Genesis 37–50). Jacob's sons were jealous of their brother Joseph and sold him into slavery. Because God was with him, Joseph was eventually elevated to second in command in Egypt.

EXODUS

I. GOD DELIVERED ISRAEL FROM EGYPTIAN BONDAGE (EXODUS 1–14).

A. God appointed MOSES to deliver the people (Exodus 3–4).

B. God sent ten PLAGUES upon the Egyptians (Exodus 7–11).

C. PASSOVER is the celebration of God passing over the Israelites when He brought death to all the firstborn children of Egypt (Exodus 12).

D. God parted the RED SEA and brought the Israelites out of Egypt (Exodus 14).

II. THE ISRAELITES GRUMBLED AND COMPLAINED WHEN THEY REFUSED TO TRUST GOD (EXODUS 15–18).

A. They were afraid they would starve and God sent quail and MANNA.

B. They were afraid they would die of thirst and God sent WATER from a rock.

C. Moses needed help and God sent JETHRO.

III. AT MOUNT SINAI, GOD DECLARED HIS PLAN FOR ISRAEL (EXODUS 19–20).

A. The Ten COMMANDMENTS gave order to life.

1. The first four commandments dealt with man's relationship to God.

a. Have no other gods.

b. Do not make for yourself an idol.

c. Do not take the Lord's name in vain.

d. Honor the Sabbath Day and keep it holy.

2. The next six commandments dealt with man's relationship to man.

a. Honor your mother and your father.

b. Do not murder.

c. Do not commit adultery.

d. Do not steal.

e. Do not bear false witness against your neighbor.

f. Do not covet.

IV. GOD GAVE INSTRUCTIONS FOR THE PEOPLE TO BUILD THE TABERNACLE (EXODUS 25–40).

A. They built the tabernacle to God's instructions.

B. At the end of Exodus, the glory of the Lord filled the tabernacle (Exodus 40:34).

C. The tabernacle was a constant reminder that God lived among them.

LEVITICUS

I. THE TABERNACLE: THE HOLY DWELLING OF GOD

A. The brazen ALTAR was directly inside the east gate in the courtyard of the tabernacle.

1. This altar represented the people's need for a blood sacrifice to approach God. Christ's sacrifice was the last sacrifice and is sufficient for us today.

B. The bronze LAVER came next in the courtyard.

1. This represented the need for cleansing from sin before approaching God.

2. Today, if we confess our sins, Christ is faithful to forgive us and cleanse us from our sins.

C. The table of SHOWBREAD held twelve loaves of bread and was inside the Holy Place on the north wall.

      1. This represented the twelve tribes of Israel.

      2. Jesus Christ is the Bread of Life.

  D. The <u>GOLDEN</u> <u>LAMPSTAND</u> burned continually and was inside the Holy Place on the south wall.

      1. This represented Jesus Christ, the Light of the World.

  E. The altar of <u>INCENSE</u> was in the Holy Place on the west wall.

      1. This represented the prayers of the saints.

      2. Christ is the intercessor of our prayers.

  F. The <u>VEIL</u> separated the Holy Place from the Most Holy place.

      1. This represented the barrier between man and God.

      2. At Christ's death the veil was torn in two from top to bottom. Now through Christ, there is no barrier between God and man.

  G. The <u>ARK</u> of the covenant was in the Most Holy Place and contained the Ten Commandments. The lid was called the mercy seat and represented the mercy of Jesus Christ.

II. THE WAY TO GOD IS THROUGH SACRIFICE (LEVITICUS 1–16).

Leviticus 1–16 records instructions for the religious life of the Israelites, how the tabernacle was to be used, the duties of the priests, and the instructions for worship, celebration, and sacrifice.

  A. The five types of sacrifice for the Israelites before Christ were:

  Voluntary

      1. <u>BURNT</u> offering

      2. <u>GRAIN</u> offering

      3. <u>PEACE</u> offering

  Compulsory

      4. <u>SIN</u> offering

5. <u>GUILT</u> offering

B. Today, Jesus is our sacrifice. John 14:6 says, "I am the way, and the truth, and the life; no one comes to the Father but through Me."

III. THE WALK WITH GOD DEMANDS HOLINESS (LEVITICUS 17–27).

Leviticus 17–27 records the laws for a life of holiness for the Israelites.

A. Leviticus 11:44 says, "Consecrate yourselves therefore, and be holy, for I am holy."

B. The concept of holiness appears eighty-four times in the book of Leviticus.

C. Leviticus 23 gives instructions for the holidays and feasts to celebrate so the Israelites would remember what God had done for them.

D. Israel was to be an example to other nations of the benefits and blessings of living a holy life in communion with a holy God.

NUMBERS

I. GOD <u>PREPARED</u> THE ISRAELITES TO ENTER THE PROMISED LAND (NUMBERS 1–10).

A. A <u>CENSUS</u> was taken.

   1. It allowed the people to see the <u>NUMBER</u> of fighting men.

   2. <u>BANNERS</u> identified each tribe.

   3. The tribes were <u>ORGANIZED</u> as God commanded.

   4. <u>TRUMPETS</u> provided camp communication.

B. The <u>CLEANSING</u> of the Camp

   1. The priests were ordained.

   2. The tabernacle was cleansed.

   3. The diseased were removed from the camp.

C. <u>COMMUNION</u> with God

   1. The Passover was celebrated.

II. God <u>prevented</u> the Israelites from entering the Promised Land (Numbers 11–21).

   A. They grumbled about the <u>food</u>.

   B. They grumbled about the <u>leadership</u>.

   C. They rebelled and refused to go into the Promised Land.

      1. God punished them by making the rebellious generation wander in the wilderness for forty years until the entire generation, except Joshua and Caleb, had all died.

      2. Yet even in the discipline, God provided for their every need.

III. God <u>prepared</u> the new generation of Israelites to enter the Promised Land (Numbers 22–36).

   A. Another <u>census</u> was taken and the number of fighting men had decreased.

   B. They <u>cleansed</u> the camp.

   C. They reestablished <u>communion</u> with God.

Deuteronomy

   I. Historical: Remembrances of the Past (Deuteronomy 1–11)

   A. Moses reminded them of man's past <u>failures</u> (Deuteronomy 1).

   B. Moses reminded them of God's past <u>faithfulness</u> (Deuteronomy 2–11).

   II. Legal: Instructions for the Future (Deuteronomy 12–30)

   A. There are two reasons to obey God's laws:

      1. Your <u>life</u> will go better.

      2. It shows our <u>love</u> for God.

   B. God's laws the people needed to obey in the land were:

      1. <u>Religious</u> laws or statutes

      2. <u>National</u> laws or judgments

3. PERSONAL laws or testimonies

III. PERSONAL: PRESENT CHOICES IMPACT THE FUTURE (DEUTERONOMY 31–34)

A. Moses' DISOBEDIENCE kept him from entering the Promised Land.

B. Moses looked into the land and DIED.

NOTES

GENESIS

1. Stuart Briscoe, *What Works When Life Doesn't* (Wheaton, Ill.: Victor, 1976), p. 9.

2. Margaret Miner and Hugh Rawson, *A Dictionary of Quotations from Shakespeare* (New York: Penguin Books, 1992), p. 145.

3. Mark Water, *The New Encyclopedia of Christian Quotations* (Grand Rapids, Mich.: Baker, 2000), p. 610.

4. Joseph P. Free, *Archaeology and Bible History* (Wheaton, Ill.: Scripture Press, 1950), p. 49.

5. Henry Vaughn, *The Revival*, www.holytrinitynewrochelle.org/yourti14378.html (accessed April 8, 2004).

6. Alice Gray, *Stories from the Heart* (Sisters, Oreg.: Multnomah, 1996), p. 263.

7. A. W. Tozer, *Pursuit of God* (Harrisburg, Pa.: Christian Publications, 1948), p. 26.

EXODUS

1. Seminar Notebook, *Walk Thru the Old Testament* (Portland, Oreg.: Walk Thru the Bible Associates, 1975), pp. 66-68.

2. Max Lucado, *The Applause of Heaven* (Dallas: Word, 1990), pp. 138-139.

3. Edmund Burke quoted in Maxie D. Dunnam, *The Communicator's Commentary: Exodus* (Dallas: Word, 1987), p. 59.

4. Ron Mehl, *The Ten(der) Commandments* (Sisters, Oreg.: Multnomah, 1998), pp. 28-29.

LEVITICUS

1. James S. Hewett, *Illustrations Unlimited* (Wheaton, Ill.: Tyndale, 1988), pp. 34-35.

2. This scenario was first suggested by G. R. Harding in *A Bird's-Eye View of the Bible*, pp. 40-41.

3. J. I. Packer, *Rediscovering Holiness* (Ann Arbor, Mich.: Servant, 1992), p. 12.

4. John Wesley quoted in Packer, pp. 12-13.

5. Packer, pp. 40-41.

NUMBERS

1. James S. Hewett, *Illustrations Unlimited* (Wheaton, Ill.: Tyndale, 1988), p. 188.

DEUTERONOMY

1. Martin Luther King Jr., www.afscme.org/about/kingspch.htm (accessed April 8, 2004).

2. J. I. Packer, *Knowing God* (Downers Grove, Ill., InterVarsity, 1973), pp. 14-15.

3. A. W. Tozer, *The Knowledge of the Holy* (New York: Harper & Row, 1961), p. 9.

LEADER'S GUIDE

1. *Webster's New Collegiate Dictionary* (Springfield, Mass.: G&C Merriam Co. Publishers, 1960), p. 237.

2. John K. Brilhart, *Effective Group Discussion* (Dubuque, Iowa: Wm. C. Brown Company Publishers, 1967), p. 26.

3. *How to Lead Small Group Bible Studies* (Colorado Springs, Colo.: NavPress, 1982), pp. 40-42.

BIOGRAPHIES

PAT HARLEY
Teacher

Pat committed her life to Jesus Christ at the age of thirty-two after He powerfully intervened and healed her broken marriage. After eight years of study, she began teaching the Bible to women, convinced that it is the Word of God that offers help and hope for women today. She is the founder and president of Big Dream Ministries, Inc. and served for eighteen years as the director of The Women's Fellowship, a former ministry to over five hundred women. She also served as the director of women's ministries at Fellowship Bible Church in Roswell, Georgia. Pat has a master of arts degree in education from Western Michigan University and has taken courses at Dallas Theological Seminary. She and her husband have two married daughters and several grandchildren.

ELEANOR LEWIS
Teacher

At the age of twenty-six, Eleanor accepted Christ for assurance of heaven. However, when her son was born with a severe birth defect, she turned to God's Word for answers and found not only a Savior but an all-powerful Lord. The Word of God came alive for her, and she began teaching and speaking at Christian women's clubs. For almost thirty years, she has taught Bible studies in churches, homes, and offices. In addition, she speaks at conferences and retreats across the country and internationally. She is president of Insights and Beginnings, Inc., which produced a video series and Bible study to help people understand their temperament types, overcome weaknesses, and use their strengths for the glory of God. Eleanor and her husband live in the Atlanta area and have a married son and one grandchild.

MARGIE RUETHER
Teacher

Though Margie was not raised in a churchgoing home, her parents committed their lives to Christ after Margie was in college. It was her mother's godly example and prayers that brought Margie to the throne of grace. Her growing love for Jesus and His Word led her to Bible Study Fellowship International, an interdenominational Christian organization in which laypeople teach Bible studies. After many years of study, she became a Substitute Teaching Leader and a member of the area team. She served there for a number of years before becoming one of the lead teachers at The Women's Fellowship in Roswell, Georgia. She has also facilitated a Bible teacher-training program for women and speaks at retreats and church conferences. She and her family live in Delaware.

LINDA SWEENEY
Teacher

Linda accepted Christ as her personal Savior when she was twelve years old. As an adult, she grew to love God's Word more and more. She began to see God change not only her life but the lives of others when they adhere to the wisdom of Scripture. Because of her passion to excite women to know the Word and to see their lives change as they respond in obedience, she began teaching the Bible to women in her church and community under God's leading. She has taught Sunday school for many years and was a much-loved Bible Study Fellowship International Teaching Leader for eight years. During that time, she not only taught hundreds of women weekly but also trained a large group of Bible Study Fellowship International leaders in her class. She has taught women's retreats and spoken at women's meetings and conferences throughout the South. She and her husband live in the Atlanta area and have a married daughter, a son, and two grandchildren.

ART VANDER VEEN
Senior Copywriter

Art began his relationship with Christ at age thirteen. In his late twenties after graduating from the University of New Mexico, he began preparing for full-time ministry. He earned a Th.M. degree from Dallas Theological Seminary and has ministered on the staff of Campus Crusade for Christ. He was one of the original team members of Walk Thru the Bible Ministries and served as chaplain for the Atlanta Falcons. In 1979, he was part of a team that founded Fellowship Bible Church in Roswell, Georgia, where he was a pastor for nearly twenty-five years. He now serves as pastor, teacher, and mentor at Little Branch Community Church in the Atlanta area. Art is passionate about helping people understand the Scriptures as the revealed truth from and about God. He and his wife Jan have three married children and seven grandchildren.

CARRIE OTT
Editor, Designer

Carrie met Christ at an early age. All her life she has had a passion for words, and as a freelance writer and designer, this passion doubles when it is words — seen, read, and grasped — that attempt to sketch a portrait of the mystery and wonder of God and His Word. Carrie identifies with Mechtild of Magdeburg, who said, "Of the heavenly things God has shown me, I can speak but a little word, no more than a honeybee can carry away on its foot from an overflowing jar." Carrie and her husband have three children and live in the Atlanta area.

To learn more about
Big Dream Ministries, Inc. and
The Amazing Collection,
visit their website at:

www.theamazingcollection.org

LEADER'S GUIDE

Leading a group Bible study can be a challenging but incredibly rewarding experience. This Leader's Guide will provide help with the "challenging" part, as you trust God to produce the "incredibly rewarding" piece.

This guide is not designed to take you step-by-step through the individual studies. Instead, it will offer some general guidance and instruction in principles and techniques. Most of what you learn here will not be specific to *The Amazing Collection* but applicable to many kinds of group study. The one exception is the section titled Suggested Formats.

Each section of this Leader's Guide will deal with a single subject, making it easier for you to return to the guide for future help and reference.

Thank you for accepting the challenge and responsibility of leading your group! We pray God will make this a rewarding and profitable experience for you.

Discussion: The Essential Component
The words *small-group Bible study* are almost synonymous with the term *discussion*. While there are very significant places and purposes for lecturing (one-way communication), for the most part a small group is not one of them. Therefore, discussion is an essential component of a successful small-group experience.

Discussion is the investigation of a subject or question by two or more people using verbal dialogue. Webster defines it as "consideration of a question in open debate; argument for the sake of arriving at truth or clearing up difficulties." Additionally, the word *discuss* and its synonyms mean "to discourse about so as to reach conclusions or to convince. Discuss also implies a sifting or examining, especially by presenting considerations pro and con."[1]

Small-group Bible studies will not always include debate or argument, but there *should* always be investigation, examination, and the reaching of at least tentative conclusions.

There are many benefits to discussion-style learning compared to lectures or even to interaction that is dominated by one person. Discussion:

- Keeps every member more involved in the learning process
- Allows for self-disclosure, enabling the participants to get to know each other better
- Helps crystallize the thinking of each group member by creating a venue in which topics can be investigated at deeper levels
- Creates a more informal atmosphere, which encourages a sense of relaxed learning
- Provides the potential of uncovering misconceptions and correcting misinformation
- Fosters more permanent learning and change because people tend to better remember what is said rather than what is thought
- Builds a sense of community as participants cooperate in their search for truth and understanding

While small-group Bible studies that foster healthy discussion will realize the above benefits, the depth of any group experience is greatly enhanced by an able leader. The leader plays an important role in helping each of these seven benefits become reality. For example, in order to keep every member more involved in the learning process, the leader will need to encourage those who tend to hide and manage those who tend to dominate. The other benefits require similar sensitivity by the leader. The remainder of this guide is intended to help the leader maximize these benefits for her small group.

But before we move on, one more issue should be addressed. While the leader is a crucial player in a small group, he or she should not become the person to whom all other participants address their remarks. One author has suggested that a discussion leader should strive to foster an "all-channel" network, rather than become the "hub" or center of a discussion wheel, as the following diagrams depict.

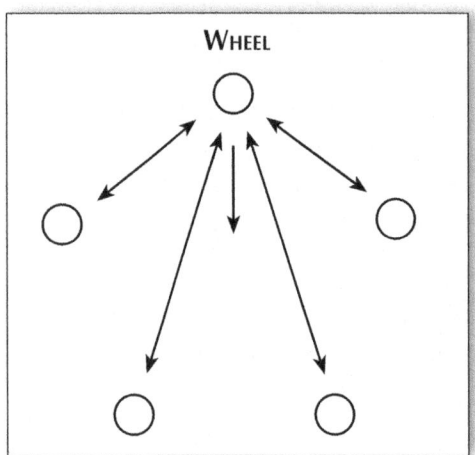

WHEEL

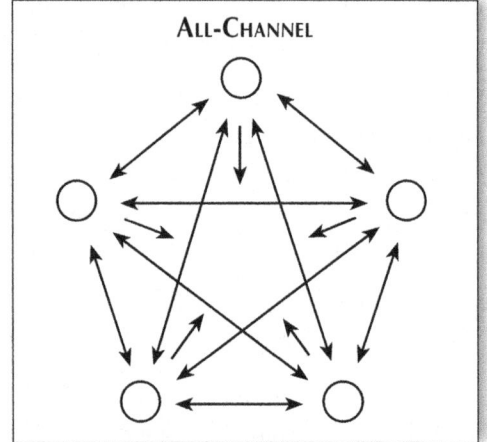

ALL-CHANNEL

LEADER'S GUIDE

In a "wheel" network, all comments are directed toward one central leader, and he or she alone speaks to the group as a whole or to any one person.

By contrast, an "all-channel" network allows rapid communication without requiring clearance from a central gatekeeper; everyone is free to share thoughts that come to mind while they are still relevant to the topic at hand. Free exchange of questions and responses is thus encouraged.[2]

The leader's responsibility is to continually remember the need for "all-channel" communication.

LISTENING: THE LOST ART

You've probably heard it said that God gave us two ears and one mouth because He wanted us to listen twice as much as we talk. It would be difficult to prove that assumption, but the Bible *does* say:

> But everyone must be quick to hear, slow to speak. (James 1:19)

> He who gives an answer before he hears,
> It is folly and shame to him. (Proverbs 18:13)

Listening may be the most powerful tool of a successful small-group leader, but it is also possibly the most difficult trait to develop. Most people tend to talk more than listen, be more concerned about their interests than the interests of others, and listen impatiently, hoping the other person will finish quickly. True listening is a lost art, which a good small-group leader must recapture.

Listening is not just hearing. As reading is to seeing, listening is to hearing. By both reading and listening, we understand the real meaning of the words our senses "take in."

Consider the following ideas and use them to evaluate your own listening habits and skills. Then, decide which areas you could intentionally improve.

Listening Characteristics:
- It is active, not passive, and therefore sometimes tiring.

- It is other-centered, not self-centered, and therefore sometimes sacrificial.

- It is crucial, not peripheral, and therefore indispensable.

- It is difficult, not easy, and therefore often neglected.

- It is scarce, not common, and therefore greatly desirable.

Listening is not *like:*

- A chess game — planning your next verbal move while the other person is talking

- A trial — judging what is said or how it is said

- A 100-yard dash — thinking how quickly you can end the discussion

Listening is like:

- A sponge — absorbing as much as possible of what is being said and the feelings behind it

- A pair of binoculars — fixing attention on and bringing into clear focus what is being said

Kinds of Questions:

- Information — "What did you do today?"

- Opinion — "Why do you think that happened?"

- Feeling — "How do you feel about that?"

Kinds of Responses:

- Clarification — "I think what you're saying is . . ." This gets at the meaning of what was said.

- Observation — "I noticed that your voice dropped when . . ." This acknowledges the importance of nonverbal cues.

- Reflection — "You seem quite sad about . . ." This acknowledges the emotional component.

- Inquiry — "Tell me more about . . ." This seeks additional information and often gleans further insight.

While you are listening, consider silently praying for wisdom:

- "God, what are you doing in this person's heart right now?"

- "Father, help me to hear what she is really saying."

- "Eternal Counselor, what kind of response do you want me to make to what this person is saying?"

There will be times as a small-group leader when you will need to limit one member's input to allow for total group input. Your aim is not to encourage never-ending dialogue with one person, but to bring the most and the best out of each participant and the group as a whole, maximizing discussion, insight, and impact more fully than you may have thought possible.

QUESTIONS: THE MENTAL CROWBARS

Good questions can spell the difference between success and failure in a small-group setting. As you lead discussions of *The Amazing Collection*, the Learning for Life discussion questions at the beginning of each study will give you an excellent starting point. But there will be times when you will want to probe differently or more deeply. At such times, forming good questions will be incredibly important.

Some of these questions may be prepared ahead of time. Others will be developed as you go. Remember, every good question shares some common characteristics:

- Brief — short and uncluttered
- Applicable — relevant to the people's needs
- Simple — easily understood
- Interesting — capable of holding attention
- Conforming — based on the material being studied

As a leader you may ask launching, guiding, and application questions. The following material describes these three types of questions, giving examples of each.

Launching Questions:
- Initiate meaningful discussion on a subject
- May be prepared ahead of time
- Will determine to a large extent the direction your discussion will take
- Are general questions intended to stimulate discussion
- Must be based on the participants' previous study to enable quality contributions
  Examples:
  - "What did you discover in this passage about . . . ?"
  - "What impressed you most about how God . . . ?"
  - "What thoughts do you have about Moses after this study?"
  - "Why do you think God included this passage in the Bible?"
  - "How would you describe the holiness of God?"

Guiding Questions:
- Keep the discussion moving, drawing out the most important ideas and refocusing a wandering discussion
- May be prepared ahead of time as you anticipate the subjects that will be raised by the group

- May be crafted as the discussion is in high gear (This takes practice!)
- Take the participants beyond initial observations and more deeply into the meaning of the material

  Examples:
  - "Sally just mentioned the concept of obedience. How does that fit with what this passage seems to say?"
  - "Who else would like to comment on that?"
  - "We've said a lot of things about grace in our discussion. If you had to boil it down to a sentence, what would you say?"
  - "What we're discussing is interesting, but we've wandered from where we want to go. Can someone take us back to where we veered off the trail?"

Application Questions:
- Are supplied for you in *The Amazing Collection* workbooks
- May be developed based on your own knowledge of the group
- May be difficult to formulate but serve as the bridge from Bible study to daily living—from the head to the heart
- Do not always involve something concrete to do or to change
- Could include meditation, reflection, remembering, or simply waiting on God
- May be questions that will encourage the group to share their answers aloud or may suggest a more private response
- May be specific or general
- Must relate to the truth the group has just studied

  Examples:
  - "Write a prayer pouring out your heart to God in response to what He has been teaching you this week."
  - "Do you know someone who models well what we have just studied? How could you affirm that person this week?"
  - "What do you sense God is asking you to do in response to your study?"
  - "What do you see in this character's life that you would like to imitate? What would that look like? What is the first step?"

Crafting and asking questions are skills that can be developed and honed. After each group meeting, it might be useful to evaluate your questions. Did they lead the group where you sensed God wanted to lead? Which "as you go" guiding questions worked well or not so well? How did the group respond to the questions? Was there any confusion? Finally, make a point to review anything you learned about asking questions each week.

ROLES PEOPLE PLAY: THE ULTIMATE CHALLENGE

If being a small-group Bible study leader involved only facilitating discussion, learning to listen well, and forging meaningful questions, the challenge would be large enough. But add to that the fact that every person in your group will have different needs, temperaments and personalities, approaches to Bible study, reasons for being there, and levels of maturity, and the role of leadership becomes exponentially more challenging.

Professor Howard Hendricks of Dallas Theological Seminary describes in *How to Lead Small Group Bible Studies* some of the roles people play in group situations. You may find these helpful in evaluating your own group's dynamic.

Immature roles

The onlooker	Content to be a silent spectator. Only nods, smiles, and frowns. Other than this, he is a passenger instead of a crew member.
The monopolizer	Brother Chatty. Rambles roughshod over the rest of the conversation with his verbal dexterity. Tenaciously clings to his right to say what he thinks — even without thinking.
The belittler	This is Mr. Gloom. He minimizes the contributions of others. Usually has three good reasons why some opinion is wrong.
The wisecrack	Feels called to a ministry of humor. Mr. Cheerio spends his time as the group playboy. Indifferent to the subject at hand, he is always ready with a clever remark.
The hitchhiker	Never had an original thought in his life. Unwilling to commit himself. Sits on the sidelines until others reach a conclusion, then jumps on the bandwagon.
The pleader	Chronically afflicted with obsessions. Always pleading for some cause or action. Feels led to share this burden frequently. One-track mind.
The sulker	Lives with a resentful mood. The group won't always agree entirely with his views, so he sulks.

Mature roles

The proposer	Initiates ideas and action. Keeps things moving.
The encourager	Brings others into the discussion. Encourages others to contribute. Emphasizes the value of their suggestions and comments. Stimulates others to greater activity by approval and recognition.

The clarifier	Has the ability to step in when confusion, chaos, and conflict occur. He defines the problem concisely. Points out the issues clearly.
The analyzer	Examines the issues closely. Weighs suggestions carefully. Never accepts anything without first thinking it through.
The explorer	Always moving into new and different areas. Probes relentlessly. Never satisfied with the obvious or the traditional viewpoints.
The mediator	Promotes harmony between members—especially those who have trouble agreeing. Seeks to find conclusions acceptable to all.
The synthesizer	Able to put the pieces together from different ideas and viewpoints.[3]

No doubt you will see some of these roles typified by members of your small group. How you deal with members who play out the immature roles and how you encourage and utilize those who take on the mature ones will be an ongoing challenge. Ask the Spirit of God to give you sensitivity, creativity, and ability as you lead. Pray for wisdom to become your constant, ready resource.

Your Leadership: A Spiritual Endeavor

Before we move on, it is important to remember that beyond understanding and fostering discussion, learning to listen well, developing your skill in fashioning questions, and learning to lead different kinds of people, it is God who supplies the grace and strength that will carry you through the challenges of leadership.

This Leader's Guide has focused so far on you and your best efforts, but in truth you will accomplish absolutely nothing of eternal value unless the Spirit of God takes your faithful efforts and infuses them with His enabling power and grace.

For this reason, we encourage you to prepare and lead in complete humility, dependence, and trust, remembering these critical precepts:

I can do all things through Him who strengthens me. (Philippians 4:13)

"My grace is sufficient for you, for power is perfected in weakness." (2 Corinthians 12:9)

"I am the vine, you are the branches; he who abides in Me and I in him, he bears much fruit, for apart from Me you can do nothing." (John 15:5)

Finally, be strong in the Lord and in the strength of His might. Put on the full armor of God, that you will be able to stand firm against the schemes of the devil. (Ephesians 6:10-11)

Our prayer for you is that of Paul's prayers for the Ephesians:

> That the God of our Lord Jesus Christ, the Father of glory, may give to you a spirit of wisdom and of revelation in the knowledge of Him. I pray that the eyes of your heart may be enlightened, so that you will know what is the hope of His calling, what are the riches of the glory of His inheritance in the saints, and what is the surpassing greatness of His power toward us who believe. These are in accordance with the working of the strength of His might. . . . [And] that He would grant you, according to the riches of His glory, to be strengthened with power through His Spirit in the inner man, so that Christ may dwell in your hearts through faith; and that you, being rooted and grounded in love, may be able to comprehend with all the saints what is the breadth and length and height and depth, and to know the love of Christ which surpasses knowledge, that you may be filled up to all the fullness of God. Now to Him who is able to do far more abundantly beyond all that we ask or think, according to the power that works within us, to Him be the glory in the church and in Christ Jesus to all generations forever and ever. Amen. (Ephesians 1:17-19; 3:16-21)

APPENDIX A

The Effective Discussion Leader: A Worthy Goal

This section presents a model for the effective discussion leader (EDL). You may not demonstrate every characteristic listed, nor do you need to. Some of these things you will do very well; others you will do okay; still others may be a weak area for you. That is just fine. Consider this list simply an ideal to aim for. Our hope is that it will motivate you to grow as a small-group leader by revealing your areas of strength and highlighting your areas of weakness for which you may need help. God never said He could use only perfect people in ministry. In fact, your limitations in one or more of these areas may allow for others in the group to come alongside and complement you by contributing their strengths.

You may choose to use this list with a group of leaders to discuss your common ministries and responsibilities and share with each other challenges and successes you've experienced as leaders. Hearing others' thoughts about each of these characteristics might encourage you as you continue to grow.

What key characteristics make an effective discussion leader?

1. EDLs have a good grasp of the material to be discussed.
   - They have studied the material in advance.
   - They have a clear purpose for the meeting.
   - They have an introduction planned.
   - They have questions planned.
   - They have a tentative conclusion in mind.
   - They have examined their own life in relation to the truth of the study.
   - They seek to be diligent workers who accurately handle the word of truth (see 2 Timothy 2:15).

2. EDLs are skilled in organizing group thinking.
   - They know how to use questions.

- They can detect tangents and gently but firmly bring the discussion back on track.

3. EDLs are open-minded.

- They express judgments in a conditional way.
- They encourage consideration of all points of view.
- They encourage open-mindedness on the part of all the members.
- They are able to handle incorrect answers by inviting further questioning or discussion.

4. EDLs are active participants.

- They talk frequently yet not excessively.
- They are not defensive or sensitive to disagreement or criticism.

5. EDLs are facilitators.

- They do not give dictatorial directions.
- They encourage participation by all.
- They encourage interaction among all members.
- They are able to manage members who tend to dominate discussion.
- They are able to stimulate and involve shy or reticent members in nonthreatening ways.

6. EDLs speak well.

- They speak clearly.
- They speak in a concise, pertinent way.
- They are not tactless, chattering, offensive speakers.

7. EDLs have respect for and sensitivity to others.

- They are empathetic.
- They do not attack others.
- They do not cause others to "lose face."
- They are aware of how others are reacting.
- They are patient.

8. EDLs are self-controlled.

- They can remain impartial when necessary.

- They can express their feelings in a direct, yet nonaccusatory manner.

9. EDLs can assume different roles.

   - They can give encouragement.
   - They can give direction when necessary.
   - They can insert humor to break the tension when appropriate.
   - They can lead the group in prayer to seek wisdom.
   - They can give personal attention to needy members.

10. EDLs give credit to the group and its members.

    - They praise the group for insights and progress.
    - They stress teamwork.
    - They make all the members feel important.
    - They value others as their equals.
    - They "do nothing from selfishness or empty conceit" but regard others as more important than themselves (Philippians 2:3).

11. EDLs are authentically transparent.

    - They share personal illustrations.
    - They share personal weaknesses, frustrations, pressures, and failures without seeking undue personal attention.
    - They share personal feelings.
    - They share personal requests.
    - They plan ahead so all this can be done with taste and genuineness.

12. EDLs are enthusiastic.

    - They pour themselves into the subject and the discussion of it.
    - They allow the subject to be poured into them by God prior to the discussion.
    - They recognize that genuine enthusiasm is a powerful motivator for others.

13. EDLs are properly critical and evaluative of their leadership.

    - They constantly look for ways to improve.
    - They regularly seek feedback and advice.
    - They consistently evaluate the various aspects of their leadership role.

- They remember that evaluation is not comparing themselves with others but is seeking the Holy Spirit's input on possible improvement.

14. EDLs know that leadership is a spiritual endeavor.

   - They regularly admit to God that apart from Him they can do nothing (see John 15:5).

   - They confidently say "I can do all things" and then humbly add "through Him who strengthens me" (Philippians 4:13).

   - They never forget God's promise that "My grace is sufficient for you" (2 Corinthians 12:9).

APPENDIX B

SUGGESTED FORMATS FOR *THE AMAZING COLLECTION*

The Amazing Collection is intentionally flexible to accommodate a variety of teaching settings and calendars. It is possible to complete the study of all sixty-six books of the Bible in two years by teaching a book a week for thirty-three weeks each year (excluding summers and holidays).

Another option would be to go through the material in three years, teaching a book a week for twenty-two weeks each year, perhaps beginning in September and going through April. Also, for individuals, the program could be completed in approximately fifteen months, studying a book a week for sixty-six consecutive weeks.

There is flexibility in each individual session as well. Sessions might last an hour, in which the group watches the video (forty-five minutes) and allows fifteen minutes for discussion. Or, a 1.5-hour format could include the video, fifteen minutes for refreshments, fifteen for discussion, and fifteen for homework review. If time permits, two-hour sessions could include the video, refreshments, thirty minutes for discussion, and thirty for homework review.

Maybe you'll discover another format that suits your group to a tee. Feel free to use it!

APPENDIX C

SHARING THE GOSPEL

Leaders should be sensitive to the fact that some group members may have an interest in the Bible without having established a personal relationship with its central figure, Jesus Christ.

Sharing the gospel is quite easy for some people and more challenging for others. But if you sense that there are members in your group who would benefit from a clear explanation of salvation, by all means, offer one! There may even be "natural" openings during your course of study (at the end of a book or workbook or during your study of the Gospels or the book of Romans) when the gospel seems to "tell itself." In addition, the vast majority of discussion questions (Old and New Testament) contain a question that points directly to the person of Jesus Christ. These are "teachable moments." Don't miss them.

Several excellent tools exist that can help you walk an unbeliever through the basics of salvation. *The Four Spiritual Laws*, *Steps to Peace with God*, *My Heart — Christ's Home*, and *The Roman Road* are just a few. The leaders in your church may be able to provide you with one or more of them.

Although there are many excellent video testimonies throughout *The Amazing Collection*, it may be appropriate at some point to briefly share your own personal testimony with your group or with one or more of its members. It may help to think of your "story" in four parts: your life before Christ, how you came to know and understand your need for forgiveness and reconciliation with God, what Christ did on your behalf on the cross, and how your life is different today having accepted His atoning sacrifice on your behalf. This is your story! Pray for a sensitive heart, the right timing, and the right words to share it when the Holy Spirit leads you to do so.

It is our prayer that no one would complete *The Amazing Collection* without a personal, saving knowledge of our Savior, the Lord Jesus Christ.

Made in the USA
Coppell, TX
13 January 2020